Polished Spiral Karin Kuhlmann

"Although the creation of fractals is bounded to strict mathematical rules, the results are always very inspiring."– **Karin Kuhlmann**

Investigations
IN NUMBER, DATA, AND SPACE®

Power Polygons™ is a trademark of ETA/Cuisenaire®.

Use of the trademark or company name implies no relationship, sponsorship, endorsement, sale, or promotion on the part of Pearson Education, Inc., or its affiliates.

Glenview, Illinois • Boston, Massachusetts
Chandler, Arizona • Upper Saddle River, New Jersey

The Investigations curriculum was developed by TERC, Cambridge, MA.

This material is based on work supported by the National Science Foundation ("NSF") under Grant No.ESI-0095450. Any opinions, findings, and conclusions or recommendations expressed in this material are those of the author(s) and do not necessarily reflect the views of the National Science Foundation.

ISBN-13: 978-0-328-62341-9

ISBN-10: 0-328-62341-5

7 8 9 10 V082 14 13

Contents

Overview

The *Differentiation and Intervention Guide* is a flexible and versatile component that supplements the *Investigations* curriculum units. An Intervention, Practice, and Extension activity is provided for every Investigation. The differentiation activities presented in this guide can be used anytime after the session referenced, such as during Math Workshops, or outside of math time. In addition, a Quiz is available to use as a formative assessment after an Investigation is completed.

Teachers may also assign multiple activities for an Investigation to a single student. For example, after a student completes the Practice activity, it may be appropriate for that student to work on the Extension activity. Similarly, Practice and Extension activities can also be used to reinforce and extend Intervention suggestions, either during the Investigation or later in the unit.

Within each curriculum unit, a feature titled "Differentiation: Supporting the Range of Learners" appears regularly. This feature offers ideas for Intervention, Extension, and ELL related to the content of that session. The *Differentiation and Intervention Guide* expands many of these existing Intervention and Extension suggestions by providing teaching suggestions and/or student masters. The *Differentiation and Intervention Guide* also provides additional Practice activities for all students.

Curriculum Unit 1, p. 20

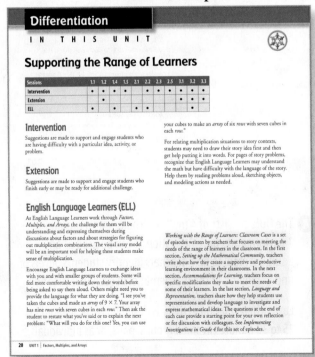

Differentiation suggestions are embedded in the curriculum units.

Curriculum Unit 1, p. 36

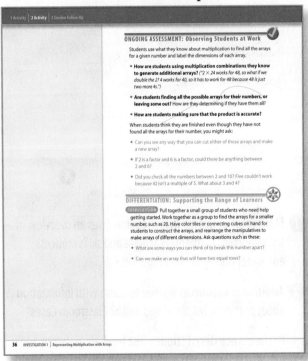

The Differentiation and Intervention Guide *enhances the existing differentiation suggestions in the curriculum units.*

Understanding This Guide

The *Differentiation and Intervention Guide* contains support pages for every Investigation in the curriculum units. The first page provides teachers with an overview of the key mathematics in the Investigation and descriptions of student performance. The remaining three pages provide easy-to-use activities based on the Math Focus Points in the Investigation. Each activity features built-in ELL support and resource masters for students.

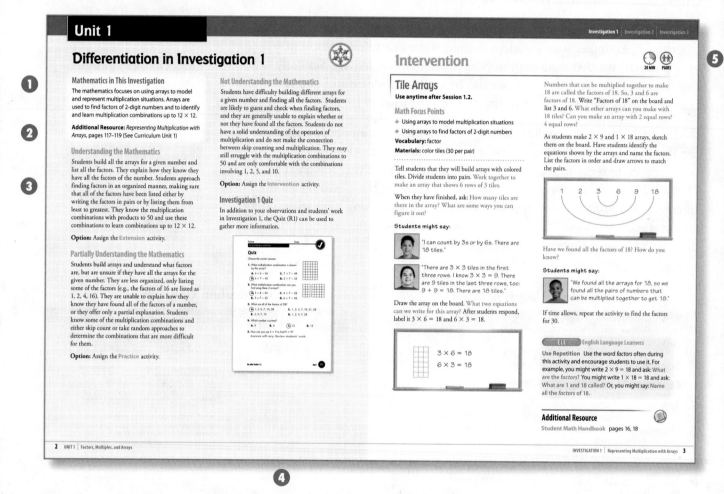

1 **Mathematics in This Investigation** gives an overview of the important mathematical ideas and skills students encounter during the Investigation.

2 **Additional Resources** provide teachers with information about pertinent Teacher Notes and/or Classroom Cases.

3 **Performance descriptions** assist teachers in determining differentiation activities based on observations of students throughout the Investigation and analyzing students' work.

4 The **Quiz** consists of 4 multiple-choice questions and 1 performance-based question. It can be used as an additional tool to help teachers identify students' levels of understanding of the mathematics in each Investigation.

5 Each differentiation activity is designed to be covered in 15 to 30 minutes in small groups, pairs, or as individuals.

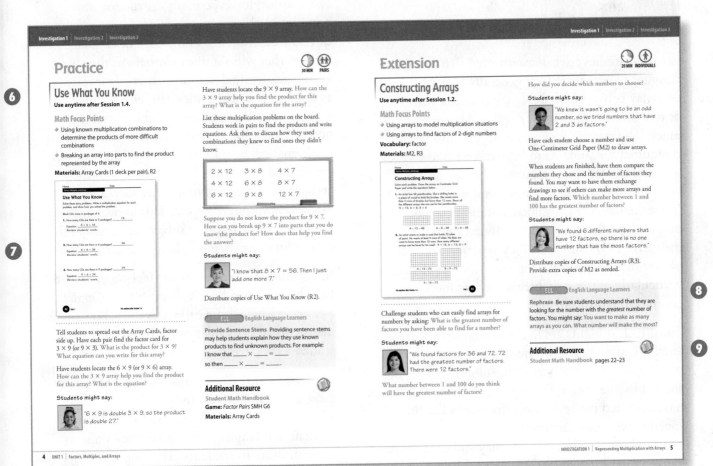

6 Activities can be used anytime after the session content is covered giving increased flexibility to teachers.

7 **Resource Masters** provide additional practice or are used as a recording sheet.

8 **ELL notes** provide teachers with suggestions to support students with language and vocabulary.

9 **Additional Resources** for students provide useful Student Math Handbook references or games to play for extra practice.

Supporting ELL Students

English Language Learners in the Math Classroom

Dr. Jim Cummins
University of Toronto

Research studies have demonstrated that English Language Learners (ELLs) generally pick up everyday conversational fluency within a year or two of starting to learn English. However, a much longer period (generally at least five years) is required for students to fully catch up to native speakers in academic language proficiency (e.g., vocabulary knowledge, reading and writing skills). In mathematics, ELL students often make good progress in acquiring basic computation skills in the early grades; however, they typically experience greater difficulty in carrying out word problems particularly as these problems become more complex linguistically in later grades.

Thus, ELL students are likely to require explicit *language* support within the classroom in order to achieve content standards in subject areas such as mathematics. Despite the fact that they have acquired conversational fluency in English together with basic mathematical vocabulary and computational skills, students may still experience gaps in their knowledge of more sophisticated vocabulary, syntax, and discourse features of mathematical language.

The linguistic challenges faced by ELL students in learning math reflect the fact that language is central to the teaching of virtually every school subject. The concepts embedded in the curriculum are inseparable from the language we use to teach these concepts to our students. For example, most mathematical problems require students to understand prepositions and logical relations that are expressed through language.

This fusion of language and content across the curriculum presents both challenges and opportunities in teaching ELL students. The challenges are to provide the instructional supports to enable ELL students to understand math content and carry out math tasks and operations. However, math instruction also provides teachers with the opportunity to extend ELL students' knowledge of language in ways that will significantly benefit their overall academic development. For example, as they learn mathematics, students are also learning that there are predictable patterns in how we form the abstract nouns that describe mathematical operations. Many of these nouns are formed by adding the suffix *–tion* to the verb, as in *add/addition, subtract/subtraction, multiply/multiplication,* etc. This knowledge can then be applied in other subject areas across the curriculum (e.g., science, language arts).

In building ELL supports for *Investigations*, we have been guided by *The Pearson ELL Curriculum Framework*, which incorporates the following five instructional principles central to teaching ELL students effectively.

1. Identify and Communicate Content and Language Objectives In planning and organizing a lesson, teachers must first identify what content and language objectives they want to communicate to students. The language objectives might include providing definitions, descriptions, examples, and visual supports for explaining vocabulary.

2. Frontload the Lesson Frontloading refers to the use of prereading or preinstructional strategies that prepare ELL students to understand new academic content. Frontloading strategies include activating prior knowledge, building background, previewing text, preteaching vocabulary, and making connections.

3. Provide Comprehensible Input Language and content that students can understand is referred to as comprehensible input. Teachers make use of nonlinguistic supports to enable students to understand language and content that would otherwise have been beyond their comprehension. Typical supports include visuals, models, and manipulatives.

4. Enable Language Production Language production complements comprehensible input and is an essential element in developing expertise in academic language. Use of both oral and written language enables students to solve problems, generate insights, express their ideas, and obtain feedback from teachers and peers.

5. Assess for Content and Language Understanding Finally, the instructional cycle flows into assessing what students have learned and then spirals upward into further development of students' content knowledge and language expertise.

These principles come to life in the *Differentiation and Intervention Guide* in the form of seven specific instructional strategies.

- **Model Thinking Aloud** When ELL students articulate their thinking processes through language, they are enabled to complete activities, identify gaps in their knowledge, and receive feedback from teachers. Teachers, however, must model this process in order for students to learn how to use it effectively. When modeling thinking aloud, it is important for teachers to use visuals and gestures.

- **Partner Talk** When it comes to working on a math activity of any kind, two heads are often better than one. Partner talk provides an audience for students' thinking aloud and an opportunity for the teacher to direct students to listen for particular vocabulary and linguistic structures as they engage in a task with their partner.

- **Provide a Word List** When students make a list of relevant vocabulary in a lesson with examples of how these words are used, it reinforces their knowledge of this vocabulary and provides an opportunity for teachers to monitor their understanding and provide additional explanation as needed. Paying special attention to homophones, such as *sum* and *some*, is particularly helpful for ELL students.

- **Provide Sentence Stems** Sentence stems provide support for ELL students to gain access to the sequence of steps in an activity, and they expand students' knowledge of how to communicate their thinking processes to the teacher and their peers.

- **Rephrase** Students struggling with vocabulary and language acquisition are often confused by extra details in word problems or overly wordy statements. Rephrasing statements in a different way that utilizes simpler language, shorter sentences, and eliminates unnecessary information helps students focus on and understand the important information needed to work through an activity.

- **Suggest a Sequence** Sequencing of steps is crucial to solving many math problems, and ELL students may need additional help in this process. Providing struggling ELL students with a sequence of steps to follow provides them with a guide for how to complete an activity or report their findings. When suggesting a sequence, be sure to use concise language.

- **Use Repetition** Repetition of instructions or explanations may also be required to enable ELL students to fully understand instruction. Because students are still in the process of learning English, they may need repetition, paraphrasing, or elaboration to understand teacher talk containing new vocabulary or structures.

Differentiation in Investigation 1

Mathematics in This Investigation

The mathematics focuses on using arrays to model and represent multiplication situations. Arrays are used to find factors of 2-digit numbers and to identify and learn multiplication combinations up to 12 × 12.

Additional Resource: *Representing Multiplication with Arrays*, pages 117–119 (See Curriculum Unit 1)

Understanding the Mathematics

Students build all the arrays for a given number and list all the factors. They explain how they know they have all the factors of the number. Students approach finding factors in an organized manner, making sure that all of the factors have been listed either by writing the factors in pairs or by listing them from least to greatest. They know the multiplication combinations with products to 50 and use these combinations to learn combinations up to 12 × 12.

Option: Assign the Extension activity.

Partially Understanding the Mathematics

Students build arrays and understand what factors are, but are unsure if they have all the arrays for the given number. They are less organized, only listing some of the factors (e.g., the factors of 16 are listed as 1, 2, 4, 16). They are unable to explain how they know they have found all of the factors of a number, or they offer only a partial explanation. Students know some of the multiplication combinations and either skip count or take random approaches to determine the combinations that are more difficult for them.

Option: Assign the Practice activity.

Not Understanding the Mathematics

Students have difficulty building different arrays for a given number and finding all the factors. Students are likely to guess and check when finding factors, and they are generally unable to explain whether or not they have found all the factors. Students do not have a solid understanding of the operation of multiplication and do not make the connection between skip counting and multiplication. They may still struggle with the multiplication combinations to 50 and are only comfortable with the combinations involving 1, 2, 5, and 10.

Option: Assign the Intervention activity.

Investigation 1 Quiz

In addition to your observations and students' work in Investigation 1, the Quiz (R1) can be used to gather more information.

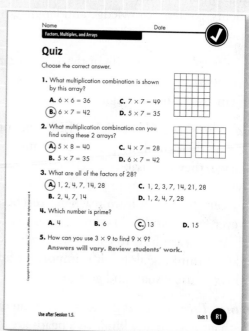

Intervention

20 MIN   PAIRS

Tile Arrays

Use anytime after Session 1.2.

Math Focus Points

◆ Using arrays to model multiplication situations

◆ Using arrays to find factors of 2-digit numbers

Vocabulary: factor

Materials: color tiles (30 per pair)

....

Tell students that they will build arrays with colored tiles. Divide students into pairs. Work together to make an array that shows 6 rows of 3 tiles.

When they have finished, ask: How many tiles are there in the array? What are some ways you can figure it out?

Students might say:

"I can count by 3s or by 6s. There are 18 tiles."

"There are 3 × 3 tiles in the first three rows. I know 3 × 3 = 9. There are 9 tiles in the last three rows, too: 9 + 9 = 18. There are 18 tiles."

Draw the array on the board. What two equations can we write for this array? After students respond, label it 3 × 6 = 18 and 6 × 3 = 18.

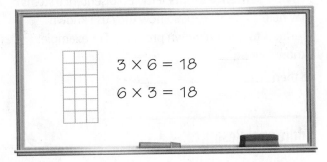

3 × 6 = 18
6 × 3 = 18

Numbers that can be multiplied together to make 18 are called the factors of 18. So, 3 and 6 are factors of 18. Write "Factors of 18" on the board and list 3 and 6. What other arrays can you make with 18 tiles? Can you make an array with 2 equal rows? 4 equal rows?

As students make 2 × 9 and 1 × 18 arrays, sketch them on the board. Have students identify the equations shown by the arrays and name the factors. List the factors in order and draw arrows to match the pairs.

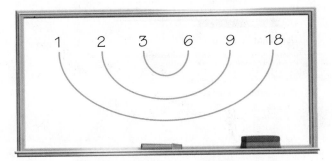

1   2   3   6   9   18

Have we found all the factors of 18? How do you know?

Students might say:

"We found all the arrays for 18, so we found all the pairs of numbers that can be multiplied together to get 18."

If time allows, repeat the activity to find the factors for 30.

ELL English Language Learners

Use Repetition Use the word *factors* often during this activity and encourage students to use it. For example, you might write 2 × 9 = 18 and ask: What are the *factors*? You might write 1 × 18 = 18 and ask: What are 1 and 18 called? Or, you might say: Name all the *factors* of 18.

Additional Resource

Student Math Handbook pages 16, 18

Practice

30 MIN **PAIRS**

Use What You Know
Use anytime after Session 1.4.

Math Focus Points

◆ Using known multiplication combinations to determine the products of more difficult combinations

◆ Breaking an array into parts to find the product represented by the array

Materials: Array Cards (1 deck per pair), R2

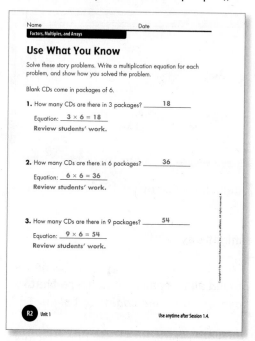

Tell students to spread out the Array Cards, factor side up. Have each pair find the factor card for 3 × 9 (or 9 × 3). What is the product for 3 × 9? What equation can you write for this array?

Have students locate the 6 × 9 (or 9 × 6) array. How can the 3 × 9 array help you find the product for this array? What is the equation?

Students might say:

"6 × 9 is double 3 × 9, so the product is double 27."

Have students locate the 9 × 9 array. How can the 3 × 9 array help you find the product for this array? What is the equation for the array?

List these multiplication problems on the board. Students work in pairs to find the products and write equations. Ask them to discuss how they used combinations they knew to find ones they didn't know.

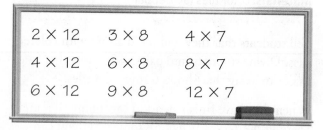

2 × 12	3 × 8	4 × 7
4 × 12	6 × 8	8 × 7
6 × 12	9 × 8	12 × 7

Suppose you do not know the product for 9 × 7. How can you break up 9 × 7 into parts that you do know the product for? How does that help you find the answer?

Students might say:

"I know that 8 × 7 = 56. Then I just add one more 7."

Distribute copies of Use What You Know (R2).

ELL English Language Learners

Provide Sentence Stems Providing sentence stems may help students explain how they use known products to find unknown products. For example:

I know that _____ × _____ = _____
so then _____ × _____ = _____.

Additional Resource

Student Math Handbook
Game: *Factor Pairs* SMH G6
Materials: Array Cards

Extension

🕐 20 MIN 👤 INDIVIDUALS

Constructing Arrays

Use anytime after Session 1.2.

Math Focus Points

◆ Using arrays to model multiplication situations

◆ Using arrays to find factors of 2-digit numbers

Vocabulary: factor

Materials: M2, R3

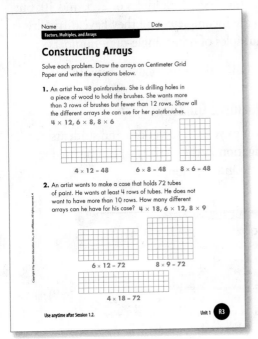

Challenge students who can easily find arrays for numbers by asking: What is the greatest number of factors you have been able to find for a number?

Students might say:

"We found factors for 36 and 72. 72 had the greatest number of factors. There were 12 factors."

What number between 1 and 100 do you think will have the greatest number of factors?

How did you decide which numbers to choose?

Students might say:

"We knew it wasn't going to be an odd number, so we tried numbers that have 2 and 3 as factors."

Have each student choose a number and use One-Centimeter Grid Paper (M2) to draw arrays.

When students are finished, have them compare the numbers they chose and the number of factors they found. You may want to have them exchange drawings to see if others can make more arrays and find more factors. Which number between 1 and 100 has the greatest number of factors?

Students might say:

"We found 6 different numbers that have 12 factors, so there is no one number that has the most factors."

Distribute copies of Constructing Arrays (R3). Provide extra copies of M2 as needed.

ELL English Language Learners

Rephrase Be sure students understand that they are looking for the number with the *greatest* number of factors. You might say: You want to make as many arrays as you can. What number will make the most?

Additional Resource

Student Math Handbook pages 22–23

Differentiation in Investigation 2

Mathematics in This Investigation

The mathematics focuses on developing fluency with the multiplication combinations to 12 × 12 by using known combinations to determine the products of more difficult combinations. Another focus is determining whether one number is a factor or multiple of another.

Additional Resource: *Learning and Assessing Multiplication Combinations*, pages 120–122 (See Curriculum Unit 1)

Understanding the Mathematics

Students are fluent with the multiplication combinations to 12 × 12. They use the terms *factor* and *multiple* correctly and can list the first 12 or more multiples of single-digit numbers. They know whether one number is a factor or multiple of another and are able to use this information when given greater numbers. Students determine if one number is a factor of another by using information they know as well as numeric reasoning (e.g., 3 is a factor of 51 because it is a factor of 30 and 21). Students also find factors by using basic characteristics of multiples.

Option: Assign the Extension activity.

Partially Understanding the Mathematics

Students know most of the multiplication combinations to 12 × 12 but may have difficulty with some of the more difficult combinations, such as 6 × 8, 7 × 8, and 6 × 9. The strategies they use to determine the products of more difficult combinations aren't always the most efficient (e.g., skip counting or writing each multiple down). Students often confuse the terms *factor* and *multiple*. Students list most of the first 12 multiples of single-digit numbers, but may miss some multiples. They know some basic characteristics of multiples, such as 5s and 10s, but are not consistently using that information to find factors.

Option: Assign the Practice activity.

Not Understanding the Mathematics

Students are still learning the multiplication combinations with products to 50. They may use skip counting or counting on their fingers for the combinations with products greater than 50. They struggle with differentiating between the terms *factor* and *multiple*. Students have difficulty determining whether one number is a factor of another and may use guess-and-check as a strategy. They might be able to list the first 12 multiples of 2, 5, and 10, but their lists are incomplete, and they have difficulty listing multiples of other single-digit numbers.

Option: Assign the Intervention activity.

Investigation 2 Quiz

In addition to your observations and students' work in Investigation 2, the Quiz (R4) can be used to gather more information.

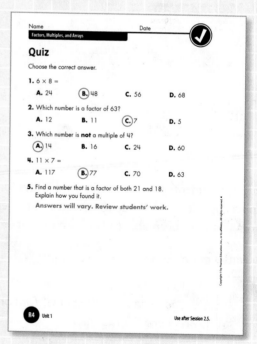

Intervention

25 MIN   PAIRS

Basic Multiple Turn Over

Use anytime after Session 2.3.

Math Focus Points

◆ Determining whether one number is a factor or multiple of another

◆ Identifying and learning multiplication combinations not yet known fluently

Vocabulary: multiple, factor

Materials: Multiple Cards 2–50 (1 deck per pair), M2, M50

For students who are still learning the multiplication combinations, grid paper drawings visually illustrate which numbers are multiples and which numbers are not multiples of a given factor. The drawings allow students to *see* the difference. Students should also be using multiples they know to reason about the numbers.

To make the game easier, students use fewer cards than are used in the intermediate game. Distribute Multiple Cards to each pair. Give a *Multiple Turn Over* Recording Sheet (M50), and One-Centimeter Grid Paper (M2) to each student.

Tell students that they are going to play another game of *Multiple Turn Over*. Review the rules of the game with students. This time, as you play the game, you have grid paper to help you determine if the numbers on your cards are multiples.

Suppose your partner calls out the factor 6. One of your cards is 42. How can you use grid paper to determine if 42 is a multiple of 6?

Have students discuss their methods and share their drawings.

Students might say:

"I know 5 × 6 = 30, so I drew that. Then I added rows of 6 until I got to 42."

Suppose your partner calls out 7. One of your cards is 27. Show how you can determine if 27 is a multiple of 7.

Students might say:

"27 makes 3 rows of 7 squares and 6 more. It is not a multiple of 7."

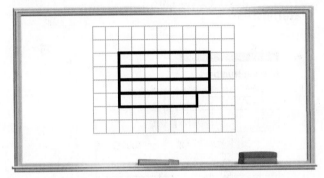

Have pairs play the basic game using the 2–50 cards. Afterward, have them compare their drawings of numbers that are multiples and numbers that are not multiples. What shape are the drawings of multiples? What shape are the drawings of numbers that are not multiples?

ELL English Language Learners

Partner Talk Have one partner call out the factor while the other partner explains their reasoning as they decide whether a number is or is not a multiple of the factor called out. Encourage them to use the words *multiple* and *factor* in their explanations.

Additional Resource

Student Math Handbook pages 24, 26

Practice

25 MIN   PAIRS

Missing Numbers

Use anytime after Session 2.5.

Math Focus Points

◆ Identifying and learning multiplication combinations not yet known fluently

◆ Determining whether one number is a factor or multiple of another

Materials: R5

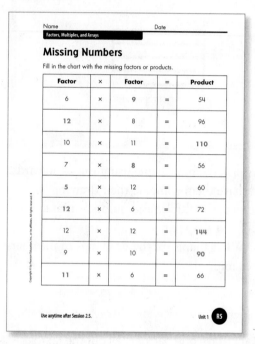

Name _____ Date _____
Factors, Multiples, and Arrays

Missing Numbers

Fill in the chart with the missing factors or products.

Factor	×	Factor	=	Product
6	×	9	=	54
12	×	8	=	96
10	×	11	=	110
7	×	8	=	56
5	×	12	=	60
12	×	6	=	72
12	×	12	=	144
9	×	10	=	90
11	×	6	=	66

Use anytime after Session 2.5.   Unit 1 R5

Write $8 \times 7 =$ _____ on the board. What are the numbers 8 and 7 in this multiplication problem called? What is the name for the missing number? Label the factors and product.

Factor	×	Factor	=	Product
8	×	7	=	____

What is the product for this equation? How can you find it if you do not *just know*?

Students might say:

"I can start with a fact I do know. I know $8 \times 5 = 40$. Then I can add two more 8s to find $8 \times 7 = 56$."

Complete the equation for 8×7 on the board. Write _____ $\times 12 = 60$ underneath.

How can you use the product and one factor to find the other factor? Have students share their methods. Then write the following equations on the board and have students work in pairs to find the missing numbers.

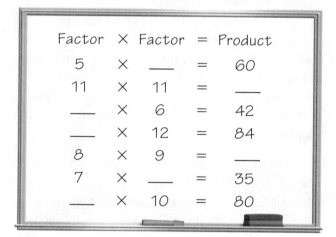

Factor	×	Factor	=	Product
5	×	___	=	60
11	×	11	=	___
___	×	6	=	42
___	×	12	=	84
8	×	9	=	___
7	×	___	=	35
___	×	10	=	80

Distribute copies of Missing Numbers (R5).

ELL **English Language Learners**

Rephrase To help students recognize that they are looking for a missing number in the equations, read the equations using *what number* for the unknown. For example: 5 times *what number* equals 60? 11 times 11 equals *what number*? Point to each number or symbol as you read.

Additional Resource

Student Math Handbook

Game: *Multiple Turn Over* SMH G9

Materials: Multiple Cards, M50

Extension

25 MIN **PAIRS**

Advanced Multiple Turn Over

Use anytime after Session 2.3.

Math Focus Points

◆ Determining whether one number is a factor or multiple of another

◆ Identifying and learning multiplication combinations not yet known fluently

Materials: Multiple Cards 2–113 (1 deck per pair), M50, R6

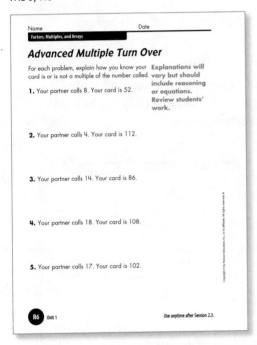

Tell students that they are going to play another game of *Multiple Turn Over.* Remind them that during the game, they have to determine if the numbers on their Multiple Cards are multiples of the factor called out.

For example, suppose 11 is called out as a factor. One of your multiple cards is 103. How can you determine if 103 is a multiple of 11?

Students might say:

"I know 9 × 11 is 99. Since 103 is only 4 more, it can't be a multiple of 11."

You can also use multiplication combinations to determine if 103 is a multiple of 11. What two equations can you use to show that 103 is between two multiples of 11? Write 11 × 9 = 99 and 11 × 10 = 110 on the board.

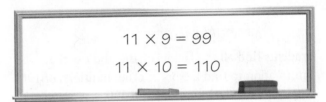

$$11 \times 9 = 99$$
$$11 \times 10 = 110$$

You know that 103 is between 99 and 110, so it is not a multiple of 11.

Distribute a deck of Multiple Cards to each pair. Give a *Multiple Turn Over* Recording Sheet (M50) to each student. Have pairs play the advanced game using the 2–113 cards. As they play, point to numbers in their hands and ask students to explain how they know whether or not that number is a multiple of the factor called. Students should use reasoning about the multiples or equations in their explanations.

Distribute copies of *Advanced Multiple Turn Over* (R6).

ELL English Language Learners

Provide Sentence Stems Have students fill in the following sentence to show that a number is between two multiples.

_____ is between multiples _____ and _____ because

_____ × _____ = _____ and _____ × _____ = _____.

Additional Resource

Student Math Handbook pages 24, 26

Differentiation in Investigation 3

Mathematics in This Investigation

The mathematics focuses on finding the factors of 100 and the factors of other multiples of 100 (200, 300, 400, and so on). The work also focuses on the relationship between the factors and multiples of related numbers.

Additional Resource: *Providing Modifications and Checking Assumptions: How Many 4s Are in 1,500?*, pages 79–80 (See *Implementing Investigations in Grade 4*)

Understanding the Mathematics

Students find all the factors of 100 and use that information to find factors of other multiples of 100. They find factors of multiples of 100 that are not factors of 100 by using a known factor to find its paired factor or by numerically reasoning about the numbers. They make deliberate choices about what numbers to choose or eliminate as possible factors. They have clear strategies in place, such as using pictures or arrays or making factor pairs, to support their thinking in finding all of the factors of 100 and other multiples of 100.

Option: Assign the Extension activity.

Partially Understanding the Mathematics

Students find the factors of 100, but may have difficulty relating that to other multiples of 100. To find factors of 200, they may use a factor of 100 that they know, such as 10, and skip count by that factor to find its paired factor. They are comfortable using only one strategy to identify the factors of 100. They use an array or picture to demonstrate all of the factors but may skip some factors.

Option: Assign the Practice activity.

Not Understanding the Mathematics

Students do not list all the factors of 100 and are unable to list the factors of the multiples of 100. Students are still developing strategies to find the factors of 100 and are not comfortable with any one particular strategy. They do not see relationships between factors of 100 and factors of multiples of 100. They try numbers randomly, or try every smaller number, as they choose possible factors. They build physical arrays, rather than visualizing possibilities, to find factors.

Option: Assign the Intervention activity.

Investigation 3 Quiz

In addition to your observations and students' work in Investigation 3, the Quiz (R7) can be used to gather more information.

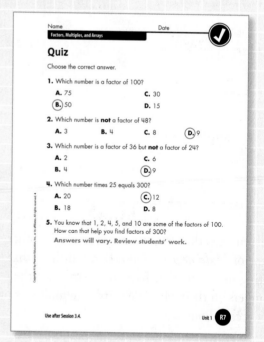

Intervention

25 MIN · PAIRS

Money Multiples

Use anytime after Session 3.2.

Math Focus Points

◆ Using knowledge of the factors of 100 to find factors of multiples of 100

◆ Using known multiplication combinations to find related multiplication combinations for a given product (e.g., if $4 \times 50 = 200$, then $8 \times 25 = 200$)

Materials: coin sets (optional)

Use the context of money to help students visualize factors of greater numbers.

Draw this chart on the whiteboard.

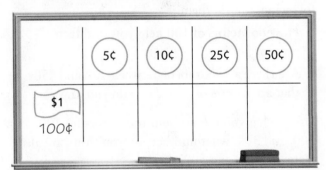

You can use money to find factor pairs for multiples of 100. You can find the number of 5s in 100 by thinking of the number of nickels in 1 dollar. How many are there? What factor pair can you write?

Write the factor pair 5×20 in the chart. Continue with the other coins. Fill in all the factor pairs for 100 (1 dollar).

You found that there are 20 nickels in 1 dollar. How can that help you find the number of dimes in 1 dollar?

Students might say:

"Two nickels make 1 dime, so it would be half of 20."

When students have found the factor pairs for 1 dollar, add another row to the chart for 2 dollars.

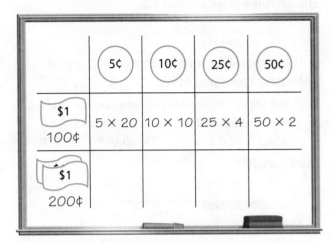

How can you use the factor pairs for 1 dollar to find the factor pairs for 2 dollars?

Students might say:

"There are 20 nickels in 1 dollar, so there are twice as many nickels in 2 dollars."

Have students fill in the factor pairs for 2 dollars. Then add rows for 3 dollars and 4 dollars.

ELL English Language Learners

Provide a Word List Write the words *nickel, dime, quarter,* and *half-dollar* on chart paper. Review with students how much each coin is worth and write the values under each word. Remind students that 1 dollar is the same as 100 cents.

Additional Resource

Student Math Handbook pages 23, 25

Practice

30 MIN | **PAIRS**

Factor Pairs and Factors

Use anytime after Session 3.2.

Math Focus Points

◆ Using knowledge of the factors of 100 to find factors of multiples of 100

◆ Using known multiplication combinations to find related multiplication combinations for a given product (e.g., if 4 × 50 = 200, then 8 × 25 = 200)

Materials: R8

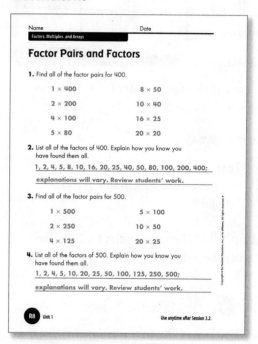

Review and reinforce what students have learned about factor pairs and factors of 100. You have been finding factor pairs for numbers that are multiples of 100, such as 200 and 300. Let's compare them to the factor pairs for 100. What are the factor pairs for 100? Write the factor pairs as students name them.

What are the factors of 100? Have students organize the factors from the factor pairs into a list of factors from least to greatest. Which of the factors of 100 are also factors of 200? Let's see what factor pairs for 200 we can make with these numbers.

Circle the factors of 100 as they are used in the factor pairs for 200. Students write the factors of 200 from least to greatest. Ask questions such as:

◆ What numbers are factors of 200 that are not factors of 100? (8, 40, 200)

◆ Are there any factors of 200 between 10 and 20? How do you know?

◆ How do you know we have found all the factor pairs for 200?

Students use the factors of 100 to find the factor pairs for 300.

What other numbers are factors of 300? How can you find them? If there is time, have students find all the factors of 300. Ask questions, such as the following, to help them.

◆ How do factors of 100 help you find factor pairs of 300?

◆ Are there any numbers between 100 and 150 that are factors of 300? How do you know?

Using what you know about the factors for 100, 200, and 300, what numbers do you think are also factors of 400 and 500?

Distribute copies of Factor Pairs and Factors (R8).

ELL **English Language Learners**

Suggest a Sequence As students search for factor pairs for 200 or 300 using factors of 100, suggest that they start with 1. For example, write 1 × ____ = 200. Have them find the factor pair; then repeat for 2 × ____ = 200, 4 × ____ = 200, 5 × ____ = 200, and 10 × ____ = 200, recording each equation as a list.

Additional Resource

Student Math Handbook pages 23, 25–26

25 MIN   PAIRS

Extension

Factor Relationships

Use anytime after Session 3.2.

Math Focus Points

◆ Using knowledge of the factors of 100 to find factors of multiples of 100

◆ Using known multiplication combinations to find related multiplication combinations for a given product (e.g., if $4 \times 50 = 200$, then $8 \times 25 = 200$)

Materials: R9

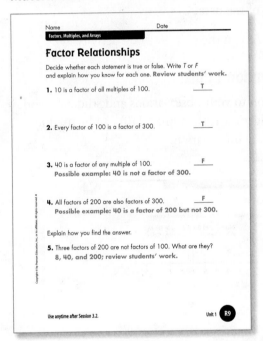

Challenge students who can easily find factors for multiples of 100 to work together to solve factor problems. Students may use their factor lists or completed homework pages, but encourage them to use reasoning instead.

You have found factors for some multiples of 100. Now let's look at the relationships among the factors.

Tell students to work in pairs to answer the following questions. Advise them that they should be ready to explain how they know that their answers are right.

◆ Is 25 a factor of every multiple of 100?

◆ Is every factor of 200 a factor of 400?

◆ Is every factor of 600 a factor of 300?

Give students time to determine their answers. Then have them share their answers and reasoning.

Students might say:

"Six hundred has itself as a factor. A number cannot have a factor bigger than itself, so 300 does not have 600 as a factor."

Now see if you can answer these questions:

◆ Are all the factors of 200 *and* all the factors of 300 factors of 600? How can you be sure you are right?

◆ There are 3 factors of 500 that are not factors of 100. What are they?

Students might say:

"Because 500 is so much bigger than 100, I looked for big numbers."

Distribute copies of Factor Relationships (R9).

ELL **English Language Learners**

Rephrase You may want to rephrase the questions and emphasize qualifying terms.

◆ Is 25 a factor of 100, 200, 300, 400, 500, and 600?

◆ Are *all* factors of 200 factors of 400?

◆ Are *all* factors of 600 factors of 300?

◆ Are factors of 200 *and* 300 factors of 600?

◆ What factors of 500 are *not* factors of 100?

Additional Resource

Student Math Handbook pages 29–34

Differentiation in Investigation 1

Mathematics in This Investigation

The mathematics focuses on representing data using a line plot for two sets of data and describing and analyzing that data. The median is used as one way to describe and compare the information within a set of data.

Additional Resource: *Data Terms and Representations,* pages 121–122 (See Curriculum Unit 2)

Understanding the Mathematics

Students accurately collect and organize the data on a line plot. To determine differences in the data, these students use the line plots and medians to tell a story about the group. They incorporate descriptions of where the data are clumped and give the highest and lowest values. They provide an in-depth description of what the data show and refer to important landmarks of the data when describing and comparing groups.

Option: Assign the Extension activity.

Partially Understanding the Mathematics

Students are correctly able to make a line plot using the data they collect, but they have difficulty seeing the data as a whole and comparing the different clumps. They are less organized and may be missing some of the data, altering the outcome of their line plots. They can determine the highest and lowest values, but other descriptions, such as median, are less obvious. Instead of describing data to tell a story, each statement is a separate statement of fact not connected to the others. Students give a general description of the data, but struggle to focus on specific landmarks.

Option: Assign the Practice activity.

Not Understanding the Mathematics

Students are not organized in collecting or representing their data and often leave out sections of the data. Their descriptions may be vague and not tied to the context of the data. Students are unable to determine the median from the data and struggle with labeling the line plot accurately, if they use a line plot at all. They are unable to use the data to tell a story and may make incorrect statements. They are not able to gather information from representations of the data and may be unable to interpret the meaning of the data.

Option: Assign the Intervention activity.

Investigation 1 Quiz

In addition to your observations and students' work in Investigation 1, the Quiz (R10) can be used to gather more information.

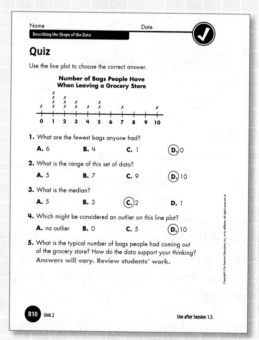

Intervention

25 MIN PAIRS

Line Plots for Heights

Use anytime after Session 1.3.

Math Focus Points

◆ Representing two sets of data in order to compare them

◆ Considering how well a data representation communicates information to an audience

Vocabulary: data

Materials: height data for Grade 4 and Grade 1 students, M6

Remind students of the line plot of their heights they made as a class in Session 1.2.

Now we want to make a line plot that shows both our heights and the heights for first graders in our school. How can we put two sets of data on one line plot?

Students might say:

"We could make the line longer and put both sets of data on it. We could make the Xs for the first graders red and the Xs for the fourth graders blue so we can tell them apart."

Sketch unnumbered lines to illustrate student ideas. If students do not suggest including a method for distinguishing between the data sets, ask:

◆ How will we know which are the heights of first graders?

◆ How will we be able to tell the two sets of data apart so we can compare them?

Help students figure out how to number the line plot for the combined data sets. Now let's think about how to number the line plot. What is the height of the shortest *first* grader? What height is the tallest *fourth* grader? So, the range of the heights is between what two numbers?

Be sure each pair of students has a copy of the two sets of data and Centimeter Grid Paper (M6). Have pairs work together to make the line for their line plot. Encourage them to work with one set of data at a time. When they have finished with a data set, ask: How do you know that you have plotted all the heights?

Ask questions to make sure students have labeled and titled their line plots. How can someone who is looking at your line plot for the first time tell what data are for first graders and what data are for fourth graders? How will they know what the numbers on your line plot mean? How will they know what the line plot is about?

ELL **English Language Learners**

Provide Sentence Stems To help students explain how to make a line plot, provide sentence stems. First, I numbered the line from _____ to _____. Next, I recorded the Grade 1 data by _____ and the Grade 4 data by _____. Finally, I _____ the line plot so it is easy to read.

Additional Resource

Student Math Handbook pages 88–89, 96

Practice

20 MIN   PAIRS

Describing Data

Use anytime after Session 1.2.

Math Focus Points

◆ Using a line plot to represent ordered numerical data

◆ Describing the shape of a set of data: where the data are spread out or concentrated, what the highest and lowest values are, what the range is, and what the outliers are

Vocabulary: range, outlier

Materials: R11

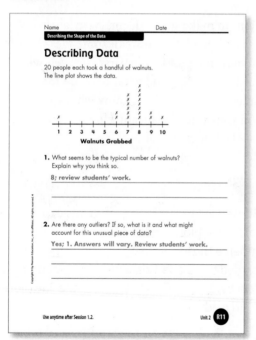

Twenty people were asked how many houseplants they have. This line plot shows the data. Draw the following line plot on the board.

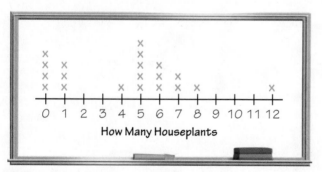

What can you tell from the data? Have students describe the data.

Students might say:

"There is a clump around 0 and 1 and a clump around 5 to 7. People have either 0 or 1 houseplants or 5 to 7 houseplants."

As needed, ask the following questions:

◆ What is the fewest/greatest number of houseplants anyone in the group has?

◆ What is the range of the data?

◆ Are the data spread out or close together? Are there any clumps?

◆ Are there any outliers?

Have students use their descriptions to draw conclusions. What conclusions can you draw about the number of houseplants people in this group have? What is a typical number?

Students might say:

"Half of the people have between 5 and 7 houseplants, so I would say 5 to 7 is the typical number of houseplants."

"The most people had was 5 houseplants, so I think 5 is the typical number."

Distribute copies of Describing Data (R11).

ELL English Language Learners

Provide a Word List Write the words *range* and *outlier* on chart paper. Using the line plot, explain the meaning of each word and how to find it. Then, have students write descriptions in their own words on a sheet of paper.

Additional Resource

Student Math Handbook pages 90–91

Extension

20 MIN   PAIRS

Statements about Data

Use anytime after Session 1.3.

Math Focus Points

◆ Representing two sets of data in order to compare them

Materials: R12

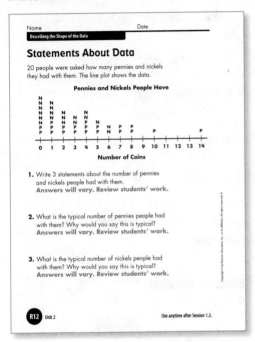

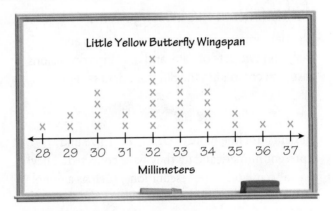

Little Yellow Butterfly Wingspan

Millimeters

Each line plot shows the wingspans of 30 butterflies. Work with your partner. Write three statements about the data. Remember to look at the range of each group of wingspans. What does the shape of each data set tell you? What is different about the two sets of data? What is the same?

Have students share their statements and observations. What is the typical wingspan for this group of Mimosa Yellow Butterflies? What is the typical wingspan for this group of Little Yellow Butterflies? If you found a Mimosa Yellow butterfly, what would you guess its wingspan to be? Why? Have students explain their reasoning.

Distribute copies of Statements About Data (R12).

ELL English Language Learners

Rephrase The word *typical* may still be unclear to some students. To help them, rephrase questions with more familiar words. What is the *most common* wingspan? What number *best describes* the wingspans?

Additional Resource

Student Math Handbook pages 96–97

Draw the following line plots on the board.

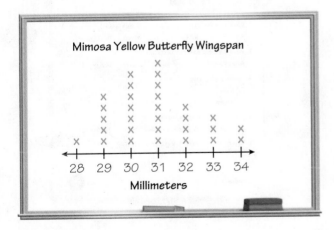

Mimosa Yellow Butterfly Wingspan

Millimeters

Unit 2

Differentiation in Investigation 2

Mathematics in This Investigation

The mathematics focuses on representing and analyzing two sets of data, and drawing conclusions based on comparing the different data sets.

Understanding the Mathematics

Students use line plots to clearly organize and represent numerical data they have collected. They may also use other representations, such as a double-bar graph, to display their data. Using the shape of the data, these students compare the two line plots and determine range, outliers, and highest and lowest values of the data. They are able to draw clear conclusions and develop arguments describing the data. Given certain characteristics (e.g., range, median, pieces of data) students can determine a possible data set and create a line plot.

Option: Assign the Extension activity.

Partially Understanding the Mathematics

Students use the results of the surveys to compare two sets of data, but they may not focus on key aspects of the data. They are able to use the shape of the data to determine where the clumps are, but they have difficulty interpreting the meaning of those clumps with respect to comparing the data of the two line plots. Their line plots are organized, but some of the data may be missing, altering students' conclusions.

Option: Assign the Practice activity.

Not Understanding the Mathematics

Students may be able to simply describe each individual set of data, but they have difficulty comparing the two different data sets. They struggle to make a line plot that includes all of the data from the different surveys, and they leave out pieces of important data, creating incorrect clumps in the data and changing what is revealed by the representation. They do not make the connection between the line plot and drawing conclusions from the data. They are unable to describe the attributes of the data (e.g., highest and lowest values, medians, outliers), and they struggle when analyzing the significance of the data.

Option: Assign the Intervention activity.

Investigation 2 Quiz

In addition to your observations and students' work in Investigation 2, the Quiz (R13) can be used to gather more information.

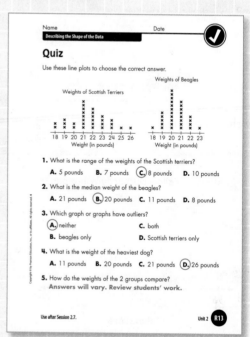

20 MIN   PAIRS

Intervention

Interpreting Line Plots
Use anytime after Session 2.6.

Math Focus Points

◆ Describing the shape of a set of data: where the data are spread out or concentrated, what the highest and lowest values are, what the range is, and what the outliers are

◆ Comparing two sets of data by using the shape and spread of the data

. . . .

Draw the following line plots on the board.

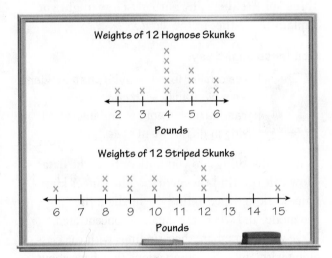

Have students work in pairs and describe each data set separately. For each data set, have them answer these questions:

◆ What is the range of the weights?

◆ Where are the data clumped?

◆ Where are the data spread out?

Remind students that median is the middle value of the data when all the data are put in numerical order. Have students model for the group how to find the median. What is the median weight of the striped skunks? What is the median weight of the hognose skunks? If another hognose skunk were weighed, how much would you expect it to weigh?

Students might say:

"Most of the hognose skunks weigh 4 or 5 pounds, so I would expect it to weigh about that."

Between what two weights are *most* of the striped skunk data?

Students might say:

"Except for one skunk that weighed 6 pounds and one that weighed 15 pounds, the weights are between 8 and 12 pounds."

Use your descriptions of the two data sets to write three statements comparing the weights of the hognose skunks to the weights of the striped skunks. Have pairs of students share their comparison statements with each other. They should check to make sure each statement is correct.

ELL ⟩ English Language Learners

Provide Sentence Stems Provide sentence stems such as the following to help students describe the data sets.

Striped Skunk:

◆ The lightest skunk weighs _____.

◆ The heaviest skunk weighs _____.

◆ The range is _____.

◆ The median weight is _____.

Additional Resource

Student Math Handbook pages 94–97

Practice

20 MIN | PAIRS

The Shape of Data

Use anytime after Session 2.6.

Math Focus Points

◆ Developing arguments based on data

◆ Describing the shape of a set of data: where the data are spread out or concentrated, what the highest and lowest values are, what the range is, and what the outliers are

Materials: R14

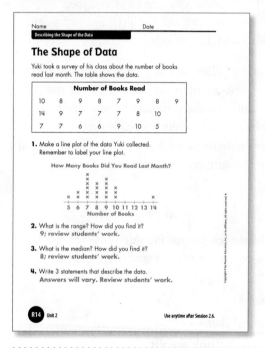

Write the data table on the board. Describe the following situation to students. Some of the Grade 4 students answered a survey about the number of states they have visited. Here are the data.

1	6	3	4	4	11
4	9	2	3	10	4
5	1	7	5	2	6
10	7	4	5	14	

Work in pairs to make a line plot of the data. Remember to give your line plot a title. How did you label your line plot?

Students might say:

"First, we found the lowest and highest values of data. That told us the lowest number and the highest number we needed to include on our line plots. We included every number from 1 to 14."

From your line plots, how many states are Grade 4 students most likely to have visited? Why do you think so? Are there any outliers? How might you explain the outlier in the data?

Students might say:

"The outlier is 14. Maybe that student has a big family with cousins, grandparents, aunts, and uncles all living in different states."

What other things do you notice about the data? How can you find the median? The range? Have pairs work together to find the median, the range, the mode, and where the data are concentrated. Have volunteers share their findings with the class, along with any other observations they have about the data.

Distribute copies of The Shape of Data (R14).

ELL **English Language Learners**

Rephrase You may want to rephrase some of the questions to simplify them. For example, ask: Are there any numbers that are much higher or much lower than the others?

Additional Resource

Student Math Handbook pages 90–93

25 MIN   PAIRS

Extension

Data Characteristics
Use anytime after Session 2.5.

Math Focus Points
◆ Using a line plot to represent ordered numerical data

◆ Using medians to compare groups

Materials: blank paper (1 sheet per pair), R15

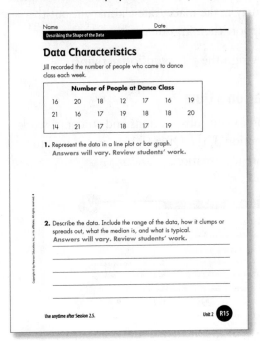

Write these characteristics on the board. These statements describe a set of data.

> There are 20 lengths in the data set.
>
> The shortest length is 22 inches.
>
> The longest length is 42 inches.
>
> The median length is 30 inches.

Work with your partner to make a line plot that would fit these data statements. What kind of data would you expect?

When the pairs have finished their graphs, compare them with those made by other pairs.

How are the data clustered in each data set? In which line plot are the data most grouped around the median? For which set of data is the median most representative of the group?

Challenge the pairs to make a line plot with the characteristics shown on the board, except no length should be equal to the median. How did you figure out how to have the median 30 without any length being 30?

Students might say:

"We left 30 empty. We made one middle length 29 and the other 31. Then we made 9 lengths less than 29 and 9 lengths greater than 31."

Have pairs make a line plot with the same characteristics except that the median is 31.5.

How did you figure out how to arrange the data to make the median 31.5? How is this line plot different from your other line plot?

Students might say:

"We had to be sure that 31.5 was halfway between the two middle lengths, so we made one middle length 31 and the other 32."

Distribute copies of Data Characteristics (R15).

ELL **English Language Learners**

Model Thinking Aloud If students have difficulty verbalizing how they made their line plots, model your thinking aloud as you demonstrate your steps. The shortest length is 22 inches so I put an X above 22. I put an X above 42 for the longest length. The median is 30, so half of the data will be less than 30 and half will be more than 30. I need to put 9 more Xs on each side to have 20 Xs in all.

Additional Resource
Student Math Handbook pages 92–93

Differentiation in Investigation 3

Mathematics in This Investigation

The mathematics focuses on describing the probability of an event using words and numbers and comparing the results of probability experiments.

Understanding the Mathematics

Students accurately determine the probability of an event and describe how likely it is to happen. They are able to characterize the probability of an event using a range of terms from *impossible* to *certain* and range of numbers from 0 to 1. They compare the actual results of an experiment with the expected probability. They are able to interpret and describe the probability data displayed on a line plot and compare the results with their predictions in order to formulate detailed conclusions.

Option: Assign the Extension activity.

Partially Understanding the Mathematics

Students determine the probability of an event but are limited in their descriptions. They can describe the probability of an event, but struggle to understand why that statement is true. They may be comfortable using such terms as *impossible* or *certain* to describe probability, but they are unable to make the connection to using numbers 0 through 1. They have trouble drawing conclusions about the probability data displayed on a line plot and have difficulty comparing their predictions with the results from the probability experiments.

Option: Assign the Practice activity.

Not Understanding the Mathematics

Students may have difficulty determining the probability of an event with the given information. They have difficulty understanding the idea of probability. They are not comfortable using such terms as *impossible* or *certain*, or using numbers to describe probability. They are uncertain of how to make reasonable predictions. They are unable to interpret the probability data displayed on a line plot, and they may make inaccurate claims without the data to support their argument.

Option: Assign the Intervention activity.

Investigation 3 Quiz

In addition to your observations and students' work in Investigation 3, the Quiz (R16) can be used to gather more information.

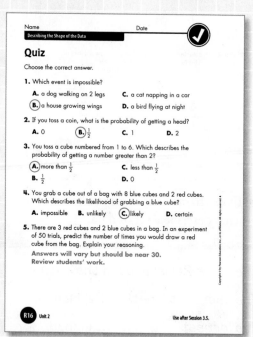

Intervention

20 MIN PAIRS

Probability and Likelihood

Use anytime after Session 3.2.

Math Focus Points

- Using numbers from 0 to 1 as measures of probability
- Associating verbal descriptions of probability with numeric descriptions
- Arranging events along a line representing the range of *certain* to *impossible*

Vocabulary: probability

Materials: connecting cubes (1 red, 3 blue per pair), bags (1 per pair)

....

Draw a likelihood line on the board.

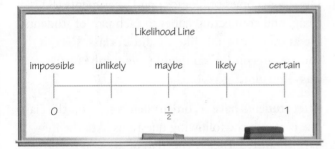

Discuss what it means for an event to be certain and another event to be impossible. Certain means that you are absolutely sure something *will* happen. For example, I am *certain* that it will snow in Colorado during the month of December. Impossible means that you are absolutely sure that something will *never* happen. For example, it is *impossible* for a duck to have 8 legs.

Demonstrate putting 1 red cube in a bag. How many cubes are in the bag? How many are red? How many are blue?

If I reach in and draw a cube, what *word* describes the likelihood that I will draw a red cube? What *number* describes the likelihood? What *word* describes the likelihood that I will draw a blue cube? What *number* describes the likelihood? Help students understand that probability is the likelihood that something will happen.

Students might say:

"There aren't any blue cubes in the bag so it is impossible to draw one. You will never get a blue cube. It will always be red."

As students watch, put more cubes into the bag. I am putting 3 blue cubes in the bag. Now there are 3 blue cubes and 1 red cube. If I reach in and pull out 1 cube, what is the probability that it will be red? Why do you think so?

Give each pair of students a bag, 1 red cube, and 3 blue cubes. Let's do an experiment. Put the cubes in the bag. Draw 1 cube, write down if it is red or blue, and then put it back in the bag. Do this experiment 40 times. Then count the number of times you drew a red cube and the number of times you drew a blue cube.

When pairs are finished, have them compare their results. How many times did you draw a red cube? Why do you think you did not all draw red the same number of times?

Students might say:

"The same thing does not happen in every experiment."

ELL) **English Language Learners**

Rephrase Some students may still be uncertain about the meaning of the word *probability*. Use *chance* instead. What number shows the *chance* of drawing a red cube?

Additional Resource

Student Math Handbook page 98

Practice

30 MIN   PAIRS

Comparing Experiments

Use anytime after Session 3.4.

Math Focus Points

◆ Comparing the expected probability of an event with the actual results of repeated trials of that event

Materials: class line plot (from Session 3.3), connecting cubes (15 red, 15 blue per pair), bags (1 per pair), R17

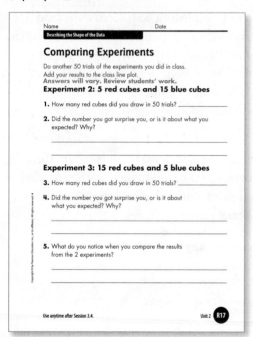

Direct students' attention to the class line plot. You did an experiment with 5 red cubes and 15 blue cubes. In your 50 trials:

◆ What is the greatest/least number of reds anyone drew?

◆ What is the median of reds drawn?

◆ How does the median compare with your predicted number of reds?

◆ Are any of the results shown on the line plot surprising?

Students might say:

 "No one got exactly 10 out of 50 red in the 5 red 15 blue experiment. I expected at least one result to be 10."

Next have students examine the results for the experiment with 15 red cubes and 5 blue cubes. Ask the following questions:

◆ What is the greatest/least number of reds anyone drew?

◆ What is the median of reds drawn?

◆ How does the median compare with your predicted number of reds?

◆ Are any of the results shown on the line plot surprising?

Distribute copies of Comparing Experiments (R17), a bag, and connecting cubes to each pair of students. Do another 50 trials like we did in class. Record your results on R17 and add your results to the class line plot.

After students have recorded their results on the class line plot, ask the following questions. Are the new data about what you expected, or are you surprised? Do you notice any changes in the shape or spread of the data? Did the range or median change for either set of data? What do you notice when you compare the results of your experiments? After the discussions, direct students to complete the next experiment with 15 red cubes and 5 blue cubes.

(**ELL**) **English Language Learners**

Suggest a Sequence You may want to provide the following steps for students to follow. *First,* grab a cube from the bag. *Next,* record what color it was. *Then,* put the cube back in the bag. Repeat until you have done this 50 times.

Additional Resource

Student Math Handbook pages 98–100

Extension

25 MIN | **PAIRS**

Predictions

Use anytime after Session 3.3.

Math Focus Points

◆ Comparing the expected probability of an event with the actual results of repeated trials of that event

Materials: class line plot, connecting cubes (15 red, 10 blue per pair), bags (1 per pair), R18

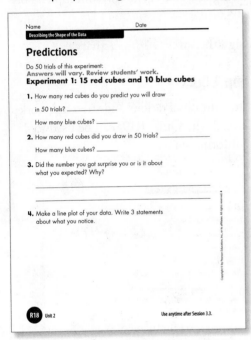

Distribute copies of Predictions (R18) to each student. Now you are going to do a different experiment. This time there will be 15 red cubes and 10 blue cubes. How does what you learned from your experiment or from the class results help you make a prediction about how many times you will draw a red cube out of 50 draws?

Students might say:

"I'm more likely to draw a red cube, so maybe 35?"

Have each group make a prediction. Then distribute a bag and connecting cubes to each pair. Check to see that each group has a plan. Who will draw the cube? How will you record your results? How will you know when you have done the experiment 50 times?

Students record answers on R18. When they are done, have students compare their results to their predictions. Did the number of red cubes you got surprise you, or is it about what you expected? What about the number of blue cubes?

In class, you did 50 trials of an experiment. You drew a cube from a bag of 10 blue cubes and 10 red cubes. Before you started, you made predictions about how many times you expected to draw a red cube in 50 trials. How did your results compare with your predictions?

Allow students to review their experiences. You recorded your results on a class line plot. Were you surprised at any of the results?

Students might say:

"One pair got 34 red. I was surprised at that."

ELL | English Language Learners

Model Thinking Aloud Students struggling to make predictions may need a model to follow. Explain that the term *prediction* is a good guess. Model making a prediction, such as: I predict I will get 10 reds. Have students make their own predictions using your model.

Additional Resource

Student Math Handbook pages 98–100

Differentiation in Investigation 1

Mathematics in This Investigation

The mathematics focuses on solving 2-digit multiplication problems by breaking the numbers apart, and on using arrays to model multiplication.

Understanding the Mathematics

Students construct and use arrays to efficiently solve multiplication problems with 2-digit numbers. They represent breaking apart multiplication problems by fitting smaller arrays together to construct larger arrays. Students solve more complex multiplication problems by combining arrays. If the problem is 14×12, they might break the numbers apart and multiply 10×12 and 4×12 to get the product. Students are comfortable using different strategies to solve multiplication problems.

Option: Assign the Extension activity.

Partially Understanding the Mathematics

Students create arrays to solve 2-digit multiplication problems, but they may have difficulty deciding how to combine arrays or break them apart to find the solution to the multiplication problem. While multiplying two 2-digit numbers, they may determine the correct product, but their solution is less efficient. They may rely on only one strategy to solve more complex problems and continue using that strategy no matter the size of the numbers.

Option: Assign the Practice activity.

Not Understanding the Mathematics

Students do not understand how to use arrays to model 2-digit multiplication. They struggle to break apart or combine arrays and often do not have a clear strategy to rely on to solve multiplication problems. They may break the numbers apart correctly, but they do not know why they are breaking the numbers apart or are unclear as to how this can help them solve the problem. Students may still be relying on skip counting as a strategy to solve multiplication problems.

Option: Assign the Intervention activity.

Investigation 1 Quiz

In addition to your observations and students' work in Investigation 1, the Quiz (R19) can be used to gather more information.

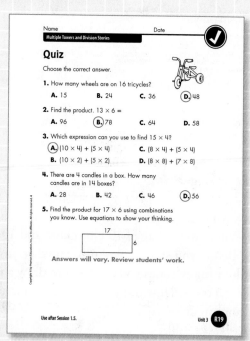

Intervention

20 MIN   PAIRS

Breaking Apart Arrays

Use anytime after Session 1.4.

Math Focus Points

◆ Developing strategies for multiplying that involve breaking apart numbers

◆ Using arrays to model multiplication

Materials: M7

Tell students that they can multiply by 2-digit numbers by using multiplication combinations they already know. They will be drawing and breaking apart arrays to multiply by 2-digit numbers. Write 3 × 16 on the board.

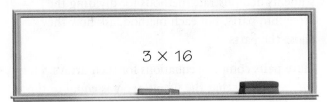

3 × 16

Distribute Centimeter Grid Paper (M7) and have students draw and label an array for the problem. How many rows does your array have? Columns?

Have pairs work together to break the array into parts. Encourage them to draw a line or lines to show the parts. As they work, ask questions such as the following: Which multiplication combinations do you know with 3 as a factor? How can you break up your array to make arrays for which you know the product? Can you break 16 into numbers that you can easily multiply by 3?

Have students label each part of their array with its multiplication combination. How can you use the combinations you know to find 3 × 16?

Students might say:

 "We separated the array into 2 same-size arrays, 3 × 8 and 3 × 8. We know 3 × 8 = 24. So we added, 24 + 24 = 48."

Did anyone use a different combination? Have volunteers share their drawings, their methods, and the multiplication combinations they used.

Next, ask students to find the product for 6 × 18. Observe the methods they use. Encourage any students who are skip counting to use multiplication combinations instead. What multiplication combination with 6 do you easily know? How can you use it to break up your array?

As they divide up their array, ask questions about their methods. Why did you choose these parts? What multiplication combination does each part show? How can you use the parts to find the product for the whole array?

Students might say:

 "We know 6 × 6, so we divided 18 into three 6s. Then we added 36 + 36 + 36 = 108."

ELL   English Language Learners

Provide Sentence Stems If students have difficulty explaining their methods, provide sentence stems. For example: My parts are _____. I chose them because _____. I used the parts to find _____ by _____.

Additional Resource

Student Math Handbook pages 18–20

Practice

20 MIN   PAIRS

Arrays and Equations
Use anytime after Session 1.4.

Math Focus Points
◆ Developing strategies for multiplying that involve breaking apart numbers
◆ Using arrays to model multiplication

Materials: blank paper or M7, R20

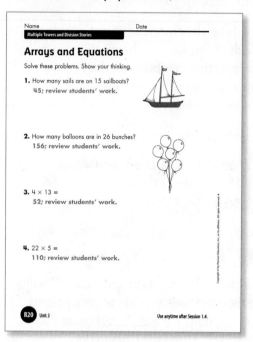

Write 21 × 4 = _____ on the board.

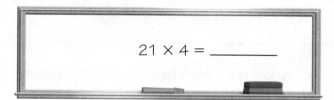

21 × 4 = _____

What array can you use to show this problem? Have pairs work together to draw an array for the problem. Students may choose to use Centimeter Grid Paper (M7) or sketch rectangles on blank paper. Remind them to label the sides.

How can you break the array into parts to find the product? Have pairs figure out ways. Then have students demonstrate methods for dividing the array into parts. For each method, ask how they chose the parts.

Have pairs complete equations for their arrays. How can you show that the whole array is equal to the two (or more) parts numerically? What is the product for each of the parts? What is the product of 21 × 4?

How many batteries are in 17 packages? How many are in 28 packages? Give pairs time to find solutions encouraging them to use what they know about 21 × 4. Then discuss their methods as a class.

Distribute copies of Arrays and Equations (R20).

Sketch a package of four batteries and the following problem on the board.

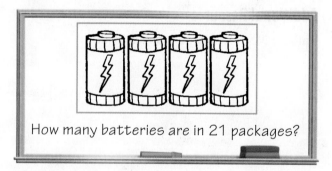

How many batteries are in 21 packages?

How many batteries are in one package? How many packages of batteries are there? How can you show this problem numerically?

ELL   English Language Learners

Provide Sentence Stems To help students write number sentences, provide sentence stems such as the following: To show the whole array, write _____ × _____ = _____. To show the sum of the two parts, write (_____ × _____) + (_____ × _____).

Additional Resource

Student Math Handbook
Game: *Small Array/Big Array* SMH G10–G11
Materials: construction paper, Array Cards, M40

Extension

20 MIN **PAIRS**

Breaking Apart Numbers

Use anytime after Session 1.1.

Math Focus Points

◆ Developing strategies for multiplying that involve breaking apart numbers

Materials: R21

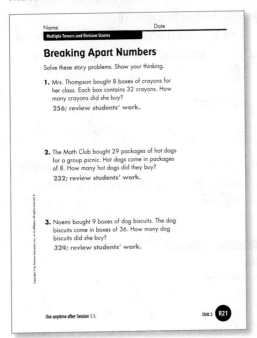

Remind students that they can solve harder multiplication problems by breaking them apart into easier problems.

Write 17 × 7 on the board.

What products do you know that have 7 as a factor? How can you use the products you know to break 17 into parts? Pairs discuss how to break up 17. Ask students how they chose to break up the 17. Record student suggestions on the board.

Ask students to find the answers of the partial product and the product for 17 × 7.

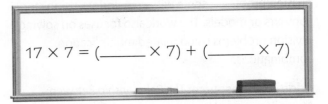

$$17 \times 7 = (\underline{\qquad} \times 7) + (\underline{\qquad} \times 7)$$

Then have pairs solve the following problems.

A band lines up in 6 rows. There are 33 musicians in each row. How many musicians are in the band?

Rolls come in packages of 8. How many rolls are in 27 packages?

As students work together, observe their strategies. Some may draw arrays, while others may break the problem into parts using just the numbers. Watch how they use multiplication notation to solve the problems. Reinforce the benefit of using 10 as one of the parts. It is easy to multiply by 10 and easy to add a number with 0 in the ones place.

Distribute copies of Breaking Apart Numbers (R21).

ELL **English Language Learners**

Rephrase Verbal questions may be challenging for some students. You may want to simplify the second problem as follows: There are 6 rows. There are 33 in each row. How many in all? Rephrase other problems, as needed.

Additional Resource

Student Math Handbook pages 16–17

Differentiation in Investigation 2

Mathematics in This Investigation

The mathematics focuses on solving and representing division problems, some with remainders, using story contexts or models. The work also focuses on solving division problems using related multiplication combinations.

Additional Resource: *The Relationship Between Multiplication and Division*, page 163 (See Curriculum Unit 3)

Understanding the Mathematics

Students efficiently solve division problems. Their work is organized and demonstrates an understanding of the operation of division. They may solve some problems by making groups of groups using known multiplication combinations. They may solve other problems by efficiently dividing parts of the dividend to create easier division problems. When solving division problems with a remainder, students make sense of the remainder in terms of the problem context.

Option: Assign the **Extension** activity.

Partially Understanding the Mathematics

Students may solve division problems correctly, but are less efficient in solving the problem. They may use either skip counting (e.g., 7, 14, 21, …), or they list all of the combinations (e.g., 7 × 1, 7 × 2, 7 × 3, …) until they have reached the target number. They create story problems, but may mix up the divisor and the dividend in the problem. They have difficulty visualizing division and may not be able to create a representation of the problem. Students are only comfortable with one strategy and need to be encouraged to try another. They can solve division problems with a remainder, but often struggle to determine its meaning in the context of the problem.

Option: Assign the **Practice** activity.

Not Understanding the Mathematics

Students may not solve division problems accurately. They use tally marks or other objects, such as cubes or color tiles, to directly model the problem. They may know some multiplication combinations, but have difficulty with understanding how arrays and groups of objects can help them solve division problems. They struggle to create a model or story context to describe the problem they are solving. When faced with a remainder, students are unable to make sense of the remainder in the context of the problem.

Option: Assign the **Intervention** activity.

Investigation 2 Quiz

In addition to your observations and students' work in Investigation 2, the Quiz (R22) can be used to gather more information.

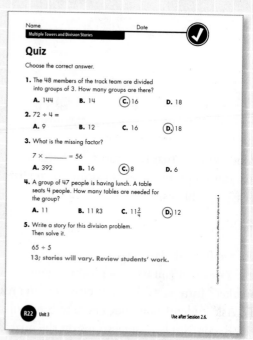

20 MIN   PAIRS

Intervention

Using Multiplication to Divide

Use anytime after Session 2.1.

Math Focus Points

◆ Solving division story problems

◆ Using and interpreting division notation

Vocabulary: division

Materials: color tiles (60 per pair)

Distribute color tiles to pairs. Then write the following problem on the board and read it aloud.

> A gardener bought 52 blueberry bushes. She wants to plant them in rows of 4. How many rows can she make?

Use the color tiles to show the 52 blueberry bushes. The gardener will put 4 blueberries in each row. Figure out how many rows of blueberry bushes she will have. When students have finished, have them share their methods for finding the number of rows.

Students might say:

"We put 4 tiles in a row and then kept making rows until the tiles were gone. We made 13 rows."

One or more of the pairs probably made a rectangular array. Point it out. You made a rectangular array. What multiplication combination does your array show? The problem you solved was a division problem. What division does the array show?

Have students help you list all the multiplication and division equations shown by the array.

> $4 \times 13 = 52$ $52 \div 4 = 13$
>
> $13 \times 4 = 52$ $52 \div 13 = 4$

Write the following problem on the board and read it aloud.

> The 51 members of a football team are running onto the field in rows of 3. How many rows of football players are there?

Have pairs work together to solve the problem. As they do so, observe their methods and encourage them to use multiplication combinations to help them. They may create arrays, or they may remove multiples of 3 from the group of 51. If they are removing groups of just 3, ask what combinations for 3 they know, pointing out that they can remove these multiples to make the problem easier.

When they have finished, discuss the following questions. What division problem have you solved? How would you show the division using numbers and symbols?

ELL **English Language Learners**

Rephrase You may want to simplify the word problems for some students by using smaller, more familiar words.

◆ Put 52 bushes in rows of 4. How many rows are there?

◆ Put 51 players in rows of 3. How many rows are there?

Additional Resource

Student Math Handbook page 35

Practice

20 MIN   PAIRS

Division Stories

Use anytime after Session 2.2.

Math Focus Points

◆ Using and interpreting division notation

◆ Solving division problems by making groups of the divisor

Materials: M7 (as needed), R23

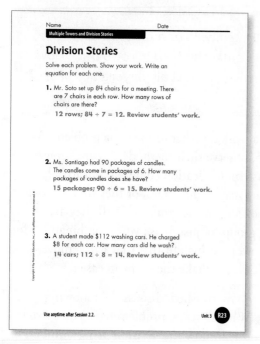

Write 7, 8, and 56 on the board, with space between the numbers.

What multiplication equations can you write with these numbers? What division equations can you write? How would you describe the connection between multiplication and division?

Students might say:

"Multiplication puts equal groups together. Division separates a number into equal groups."

Label the factors and product in a multiplication equation and the divisor, dividend, and quotient in a division equation. Then read the following problem aloud.

> Mr. Rice bought a box of 72 bolts. He uses 6 bolts for each swing seat he makes. How many swing seats can he make with the 72 bolts?

Is this a multiplication situation or a division situation? What equation will you use to solve the problem? Students might use either $6 \times$ _____ $= 72$ or $72 \div 6 =$ _____.

Students work in pairs to answer the question, using equations to show their solution. Allow them to use Centimeter Grid Paper (M7) if desired. What multiplication combinations do you know that will help you solve the division problem?

Point out multiples of 10. You used 10 times 6 as your starting point. How did this help you find the quotient? Why might 10 times the divisor be a good place to start?

Distribute copies of Division Stories (R23).

ELL **English Language Learners**

Provide a Word List To reinforce the names for the parts of multiplication and division equations, have students label their own equations with *factor, product, divisor, dividend,* and *quotient.*

Additional Resource

Student Math Handbook
Game: *Missing Factors* SMH G8
Materials: Array cards, M45

20 MIN   PAIRS

Extension

Making Sense of Remainders

Use anytime after Session 2.4.

Math Focus Points

◆ Solving division problems by making groups of the divisor

◆ Making sense of remainders in terms of the problem context

Materials: R24

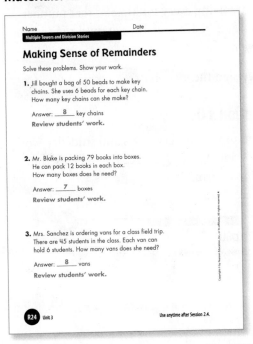

Write the following on the board.

> Equation: $63 \div 4 = 15\frac{3}{4}$
>
> Answer: 16

What do you know about the problem by looking at its equation and answer?

Students might say:

"I have to divide 63 by 4. I get 15 fours and have 3 left over. The answer is 16 because 63 things need to be included, so I must add one more to 15."

Have pairs work together to write a word problem that fits the equation and its answer. Ask them to share their word problem. Discuss whether each problem fits both the equation and answer. Then have pairs solve the following problems.

> Anna has 63 books. She wants to put 4 books on each shelf. How many shelves will she need?
>
> Luke has 63 pounds of peanuts. He is filling 4-pound bags of peanuts. How many bags can he fill?

Both problems used the same numbers. The quotient for each problem is the same. How are the remainders treated in each problem? Why are the answers not the same?

Distribute copies of Making Sense of Remainders (R24).

English Language Learners

Model Thinking Aloud Verbalizing the differences in the way the remainder is treated may prove challenging for some students. Help students by modeling your thinking aloud for interpreting remainders. For example: I know that Anna can fill 15 shelves with books but will have 3 books left. She needs another shelf for those books. So, Anna needs 16 shelves. Repeat for Luke's bags of peanuts.

Additional Resource

Student Math Handbook pages 48–49

Differentiation in Investigation 3

Mathematics in This Investigation

The mathematics focuses on understanding the effect of multiplying by a multiple of 10, and on multiplying 2-digit numbers by multiples of 10.

Understanding the Mathematics

Students efficiently solve multiplication problems with multiples of 10. They are clear in describing the relationship between such expressions as 3×4 and 3×40, and they can explain that "adding a zero" really means multiplying one of the factors by 10. They can identify more difficult multiples (e.g., the 12th multiple) by using the 10th multiple of that number and adding the remaining multiples to find the answer. They easily solve multiplication problems with 2-digit numbers.

Option: Assign the Extension activity.

Partially Understanding the Mathematics

Students correctly solve multiplication problems with multiples of 10, but may refer to the 300 charts from time to time for support. They "add a zero" when multiplying by a multiple of 10, but struggle to explain why this works. To find more difficult multiples beyond 10, students might skip count to find their answer. They often use only one strategy when multiplying 2-digit numbers, which does not necessarily involve using a multiple of 10.

Option: Assign the Practice activity.

Not Understanding the Mathematics

Students have difficulty solving multiplication problems using multiples of 10. They may ultimately come to a correct answer, but their strategies are less efficient and they are most comfortable using skip counting as a strategy. These students may "add a zero" when multiplying by 10 because they recognize a pattern, but are unable to explain why they can do this. These students find it challenging to identify efficient ways to find multiples beyond 10 and may rely on multiplying every multiple of that number (e.g., 1×12, 2×12, 3×12, …) until they reach their answer.

Option: Assign the Intervention activity.

Investigation 3 Quiz

In addition to your observations and students' work in Investigation 3, the Quiz (R25) can be used to gather more information.

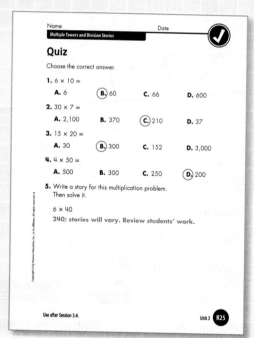

Intervention

25 MIN   **PAIRS**

Multiplying a Multiple of 10
Use anytime after Session 3.1.

Math Focus Points
◆ Finding multiples of 2-digit numbers

Vocabulary: multiple

Materials: towers constructed during class

. . . .

If a pair of students made a multiple tower for 20, use it. If not, choose a tower for 40 or 50 and adjust the activity. What number was used to make the tower? How do you know?

How many multiples are in the tower? If students count to find the number of multiples, ask: How can you figure out the number of multiples without counting one by one?

Students might say:

"20 times 10 is 200, so I started there and counted on from 10."

What equation shows the product of 20 and the number of multiples? Have a volunteer write the equation on the board. Then list multiples of 20. How can you use multiplication combinations you know to find these products?

$$20 \times 16 = 320$$
$$20 \times 2 = \qquad 20 \times 3 = \qquad 20 \times 5 =$$

Students might say:

"I would use the multiplication combinations for 2. I would find the products for 2 times the number. Then I would put a zero on the end because I am multiplying by 20, not 2."

Does anyone else have another method for finding the products? How would you find the product for 20×14?

Students should recognize that they can break up 14 and use products they have already found, for example, adding the products for 20×10 and 20×4. They may also use repeated addition or skip counting, but help them see that these methods are less efficient.

Write the following problems on the board and have pairs work together to write the products. Discuss how they can use 20×10 to find the other products.

$$20 \times 10 =$$
$$20 \times 20 =$$
$$20 \times 25 =$$

When students have finished, have them compare methods for finding the products.

Provide a Word List Some students may struggle with the word *multiple*. Review the meaning with students. Then, write 10, 20, 30, 40, 50, 60, 70, 80, and 90 on the board. If I skip count by 10 to 90, these are the numbers I would say. These are *multiples* of 10.

Additional Resource

Student Math Handbook pages 36–38

Practice

20 MIN   PAIRS

Multiplication Stories

Use anytime after Session 3.3.

Math Focus Points

◆ Multiplying multiples of 10

Materials: R26

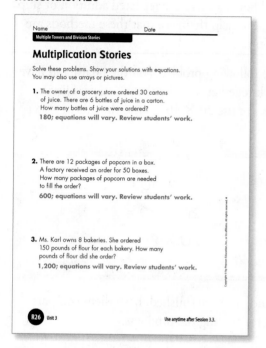

Read the following problem aloud. A dog owner buys 12 boxes of dog biscuits. Each box has 30 biscuits. How many dog biscuits were bought?

What equation can you write for this problem? Have pairs work together to solve the problem and use equations to show their solutions.

As they work, remind students to look for ways to make the problem easier by multiplying by 10. They may choose to break apart the numbers in a variety of ways. Some students may also draw pictures to help them visualize the problem.

When students have finished, have them share their strategies. How did you find the product? What equations did you use?

Students might say:

"We multiplied 3 × 10 and then used it to find 30 × 10. Then we multiplied 3 × 2 and used it to find 30 × 2. Last, we added 300 + 60. The owner bought 360 dog biscuits."

$$3 \times 10 = 30 \rightarrow 30 \times 10 = 300$$
$$3 \times 2 = 6 \rightarrow 30 \times 2 = 60$$
$$300 + 60 = 360$$
$$30 \times 12 = 360$$

Students might say:

"We broke 30 into 3 tens. Then we multiplied 10 × 12 and added 120 three times. The owner bought 360 dog treats."

$$30 = 10 + 10 + 10$$
$$10 \times 12 = 120$$
$$120 + 120 + 120 = 360$$
$$30 \times 12 = 360$$

Distribute copies of Multiplication Stories (R26).

ELL **English Language Learners**

Suggest a Sequence If students have difficulty explaining their methods, help them sequence their steps. For example: What did you do *first*? What equation can you write to show that? What did you do *next*? Write that as an equation. What was your *last* step? What is the equation?

Additional Resource

Student Math Handbook pages 36–38

Extension

25 MIN   PAIRS

About Multiples

Use anytime after Session 3.2.

Math Focus Points

◆ Understanding the effect of multiplying by a multiple of 10 (e.g., describing the relationship between 3 × 4 and 3 × 40)

Materials: adding machine tape, inch/centimeter rulers, calculators, R27

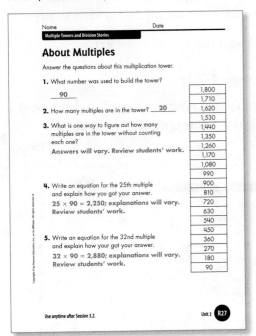

Challenge students to use what they have learned about multiplying by a multiple of 10 to find multiples for 110, 120, 130, and so on. Assign pairs one of these numbers and have them work together to make a tower showing the first 30 multiples of their number.

As they work, ask questions such as the following:

◆ How did you find 110 × 2?

◆ How did you find 120 × 20?

◆ How can you use the product for 130 × 10 to find the product for 130 × 20?

◆ Are you using a pattern to find multiples? What is the pattern?

When pairs are finished, have them share their methods for finding multiples. How did you find the first 9 products for your tower?

Students might say:

"Our number is 120. We used the multiplication combinations for 12 to find the first 9 numbers."

How did you find the product for 14 times your number? How did you find the product for 25 times your number?

Students might say:

"We added the products 20 × 120 = 2,400 and 5 × 120 = 600 to get 25 × 120 = 3,000."

How is the product for 13 × 18 related to the product of 130 × 18? If you know that 12 × 3 = 36, how can you use that to find the products for 120 × 3 and 120 × 30?

Distribute copies of About Multiples (R27).

Additional Resource

Student Math Handbook pages 36–38

Differentiation in Investigation 4

Mathematics in This Investigation

The mathematics focuses on solving multiplication problems with greater 2-digit numbers by breaking the numbers apart. Other multiplication strategies may also be used.

Additional Resource: *The Case of Kevin and Dejara: Multiplying by Multiples of 10,* pages 83–86 (See *Implementing Investigations in Grade 4*)

Understanding the Mathematics

Students solve multiplication problems fluently with greater 2-digit numbers. They use different contexts and representations, including arrays, to show their understanding of multiplication. Students are able to keep track of what part of the problem they have solved and what still remains to be solved. They use the appropriate problems in a cluster to support their solution to the given multiplication problem. They are also able to solve a multiplication problem when given a first step. Students are comfortable using multiplication combinations, multiples of 10, or other strategies using related multiplication problems.

Option: Assign the Extension activity.

Partially Understanding the Mathematics

Students correctly solve greater 2-digit multiplication problems by breaking the numbers apart, but they may not understand why breaking the numbers apart can be a helpful strategy. They may choose to break the numbers apart in ways that are difficult to follow, making it hard to keep track of what parts have been solved and what remains. They may not always efficiently choose the cluster problems that help them get to the answer, and they may not see how the cluster problems and solution are related. These students generally rely on one strategy for solving multiplication problems.

Option: Assign the Practice activity.

Not Understanding the Mathematics

Students struggle to solve 2-digit multiplication problems by breaking the numbers apart. They have difficulty seeing how a problem can be broken up into smaller parts and used to solve the given problem. They see the cluster problems as individual problems to solve, and they do not see the relationship between solving the cluster problems and breaking the numbers apart. They use the same strategy when solving multiplication problems and may have a difficult time explaining their strategy.

Option: Assign the Intervention activity.

Investigation 4 Quiz

In addition to your observations and students' work in Investigation 4, the Quiz (R28) can be used to gather more information.

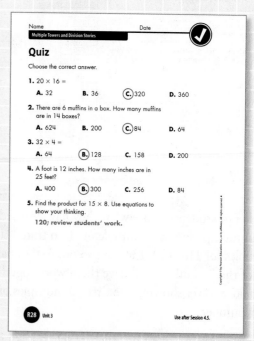

Intervention

20 MIN · PAIRS

Breaking Numbers into Tens and Ones

Use anytime after Session 4.3.

Math Focus Points

◆ Developing strategies for multiplying that involve breaking apart numbers

To help students understand multiplication and find the solution to 24 × 6, put it in context by introducing the following story.

> Ms. Grant bought 24 boxes of glasses for her restaurant. There are 6 glasses in each box. How many glasses did she buy?

Help students think about what the problem is asking. How many glasses are in each box? How many boxes are there? What operation will you use to find the answer? What equation can you write?

There are many ways to solve this problem. What are some ways we might break these numbers apart?

Students might say:

"I can break 24 into 10 + 10 + 4. 10 × 6 = 60 so I add 60 + 60. That's 120. 6 × 4 is 24. 120 + 24 = 144."

Then guide students through breaking up the problem. What part of 24 × 6 is 10 × 6? How can solving 10 × 6 help you solve the problem? What other products do you need to find?

Does anyone have a different strategy for solving this problem?

Students might say:

"I know 24 × 2 = 48. So I can add 48 + 48 + 48. She bought 144 glasses."

Have pairs of students find the number of glasses in 18 boxes and in 32 boxes. Write each equation you use to solve the problem.

Watch to see what strategies students use. Encourage them to break up the numbers using place value or multiplication combinations they know. Ask questions such as the following:

◆ Why did you break apart the numbers that way?

◆ What multiplication combinations for 6 do you know that you can use to find the product?

◆ How much of the problem have you solved? What do you still have to solve?

ELL English Language Learners

Use Repetition Using a 24 × 6 array, illustrate the problem for students. As you reread the problem, point to each part of the array, showing the 24 boxes (the 24 columns of the array) and the 6 glasses per box (6 rows of the array). As students suggest how to break up the problem (10 × 6), draw and label each part on the array.

Additional Resource

Student Math Handbook pages 40–41

Practice

20 MIN · PAIRS

Multiplication Strategies

Use anytime after Session 4.3.

Math Focus Points

◆ Developing strategies for multiplying that involve breaking apart numbers

Materials: R29

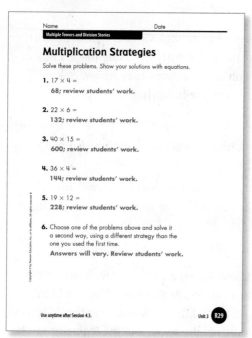

Show the following strategies for finding 28 × 5.

$28 \times 5 = 14 \times 10$ $= 140$	$10 \times 5 = 50$
	$10 \times 5 = 50$
$25 \times 5 = 125$	$8 \times 5 = 40$
$3 \times 5 = 15$	$50 + 50 + 40$
$125 + 15 = 140$	$= 140$

These are ways three people found the product for 28 × 5. How did each person do it? Have students explain each method and why it works.

Students might say:

"28 is 25 + 3, so if you multiply them both by 5 and add them, you'll get the answer."

Can you think of any other ways to find the product for 28 × 5?

Students might say:

"I would break 28 into 20 and 8. Then 20 × 5 = 100 and 8 × 5 = 40. The sum is 140, so 28 × 5 = 140."

Have students work in pairs to find the products for 25 × 8 and 16 × 9. Encourage students to use the biggest chunks of the numbers they can. Show your solutions with equations.

When students are finished, have them share their methods. Emphasize the fact that there are many ways to break up numbers to make them easier to multiply.

Distribute copies of Multiplication Strategies (R29).

ELL **English Language Learners**

Provide Sentence Stems Some English Language Learners may have difficulty explaining their methods. Help them by providing sentence stems. For example: First, I broke _____ into _____. Next, I found the _____ (product) for each part. Then, I _____ (added) the products.

Additional Resource

Student Math Handbook pages 40–41

Extension

20 MIN **PAIRS**

Pairs of Problems

Use anytime after Session 4.1.

Math Focus Points

◆ Determining the effect on the product when a factor is doubled or halved

Materials: R30

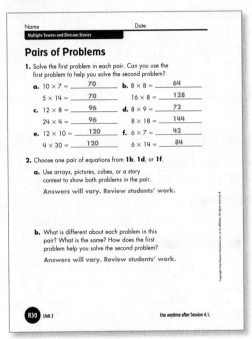

Review doubling and halving when solving a multiplication problem. Write $140 \times 2 =$ _____ and $70 \times 4 =$ _____ on the board.

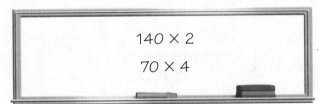

$$140 \times 2$$
$$70 \times 4$$

What are the products for these two problems? When students have figured out the products, have them share their methods. What is the relationship between the numbers in these two problems? What multiplication strategy do the two problems illustrate?

Students might say:

"You can halve one factor and double the other and get the same product."

When might you use this strategy? Have partners share their thoughts.

Then show these problems on the board.

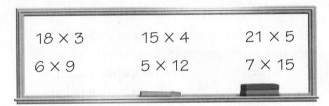

$$18 \times 3 \qquad 15 \times 4 \qquad 21 \times 5$$
$$6 \times 9 \qquad 5 \times 12 \qquad 7 \times 15$$

Have pairs of students find the products. How are the two problems in each pair the same? How are they different? What is the relationship between the numbers in each pair of problems?

Students might say:

"For each set, one factor in the second problem is tripled and the other is $\frac{1}{3}$ of the number in the first problem."

Do you think you can use this as a multiplication strategy? Why? After students have time to discuss, distribute copies of Pairs of Problems (R30).

ELL ▶ **English Language Learners**

Model Thinking Aloud Verbalize the relationships among the numbers in 18×3 and 6×9 and then have students use the same terminology to verbalize the relationships among the numbers in the other two problems. Six is $\frac{1}{3}$ of 18. Nine is triple 3, or 3×3.

Additional Resource

Student Math Handbook pages 40–43

Differentiation in Investigation 1

Mathematics in This Investigation

The mathematics focuses on measuring length using both U. S. standard units and metric units. The work also focuses on measuring the perimeter of a shape.

Additional Resource: *The Case of Norma: Understanding the Relationship Between Feet and Yards*, pages 76–77 (See *Implementing Investigations in Grade 4*)

Understanding the Mathematics

Students read and use rulers, meter sticks, and measuring tape accurately, always starting from 0. They make reasonable estimates when measuring length. They are comfortable measuring in both U.S. standard units and metric units and can distinguish the difference between the two. Students measure lengths up to 100 feet and longer and find alternate paths. They understand perimeter and easily find the perimeter of different objects in the classroom.

Option: Assign the Extension activity.

Partially Understanding the Mathematics

Students measure to 100 feet, but they may struggle with longer distances. They are most comfortable using only one measurement tool and may have difficulty using other tools to measure, particularly if they are only given one of that tool when measuring. They may always start their measurements from 0, but may have other inaccuracies in their measurement. They generally are only comfortable using the U.S. standard units and only use the metric system when specifically asked to do so. They may sometimes get the two systems confused. Students are developing their understanding of perimeter.

Option: Assign the Practice activity.

Not Understanding the Mathematics

Students are not able to measure accurately to 100 feet. They are often only comfortable with a ruler, which causes difficulty with measuring lengths greater than 12 inches. They may not always start their measurements at 0, and they make careless mistakes when measuring the length of an object. These students are not comfortable using the metric system for measurement, often confusing the metric system with the U.S. standard system. Finding the perimeter of an object is a challenge for this group of students.

Option: Assign the Intervention activity.

Investigation 1 Quiz

In addition to your observations and students' work in Investigation 1, the Quiz (R31) can be used to gather more information.

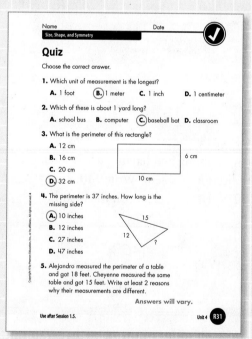

Intervention

20 MIN   **PAIRS**

Measuring Length

Use anytime after Session 1.2.

Math Focus Points

◆ Using U.S. standard and metric units to accurately measure length

Materials: 12-inch rulers (2 per pair)

. . . .

Tell students that they will use rulers to practice measuring. Give each pair of students 2 rulers. How many inches long is each ruler? If you put 2 rulers together, how many inches is that?

Sketch a line on the board that is about 18 inches long. About how long do you think this line is? Is it more or less than 12 inches?

Let me measure this line. Hold the 2 rulers as shown below. It looks like the line is about 15 inches. What do you think?

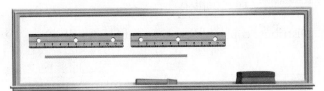

Students might say:

"No. The ends of the rulers have to touch."

"The left end of the ruler is at the 2. The end of the ruler has to line up with the beginning of the line."

Have a pair of students come to the board to measure the line. Ask the other students if they agree the pair is measuring correctly. Work with students to record the length of the line in inches and in feet and inches.

Refer to page 103 in the *Student Math Handbook* for other examples of common measurement errors. Remember these important rules: keep the rulers in a straight line, start measuring with 0, make sure the rulers touch end-to-end, and do not let the rulers overlap.

Have students practice measuring objects less than 2 feet long. Encourage them to first make estimates and then use the rulers to check.

ELL **English Language Learners**

Model Thinking Aloud Some students may have trouble verbalizing an *estimate*. Demonstrate making an *estimate* using classroom objects while you model your thinking aloud. For example: I think this tissue box is close to 6 inches. My *estimate* is 6 inches. I think this pencil case is close to 10 inches. My *estimate* is 10 inches.

Additional Resource

Student Math Handbook pages 101–103

Practice

15 MIN | **INDIVIDUALS**

Perimeters of Shapes

Use anytime after Session 1.5.

Math Focus Points

◆ Finding perimeter using standard units

Vocabulary: perimeter, feet

Materials: R32

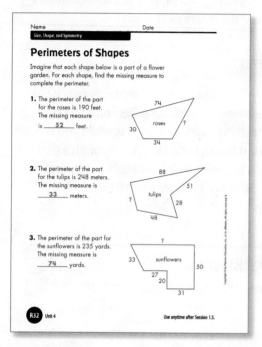

Allow students a minute to study the drawing of the flower garden, and to think about how to determine the length of the missing side. How can we find the length of the missing side?

Students might say:

> "I know the whole way around is 118 feet. I can add the three sides I know and then subtract that from 118."

Let's use what we know. What is the sum of the three sides we know? What do we do next?

Have students do the computation to find that the missing side is 36 feet. Does 36 feet seem to be a reasonable answer? Why or why not?

Students might say:

> "The missing side should be longer than 17 or 23. But, it should be shorter than 42. So, 36 feet seems reasonable."

Distribute copies of Perimeters of Shapes (R32).

ELL **English Language Learners**

Rephrase The meaning of *perimeter* may still be unclear to some students. Rephrase using other ways to describe the same idea, using pointing and gestures to support each description. For example: *Perimeter* is the distance around. It is the length of the entire border of the shape. It is the sum of all the edge lengths. Think about walking around the edges. The *perimeter* tells how far you walk.

Additional Resource

Student Math Handbook pages 104–105

Draw a shape on the board. This shape represents part of a large flower garden.

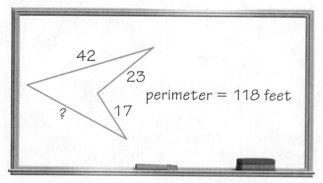

This part of the garden is for the daisies. The perimeter is 118 feet. One measure is missing.

Ask students the meaning of perimeter. If students don't remember, remind them that it is the measure of the length of the outside edge of an object.

Extension

30 MIN   PAIRS

Finding Perimeters

Use anytime after Session 1.4.

Math Focus Points

◆ Using U.S. standard and metric units to accurately measure length

◆ Finding perimeter using standard units

Vocabulary: yard, perimeter, yardstick, foot

Materials: masking tape, yardstick, R33

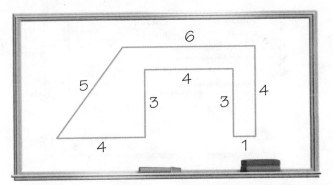

Draw this 30-yard closed path on the board.

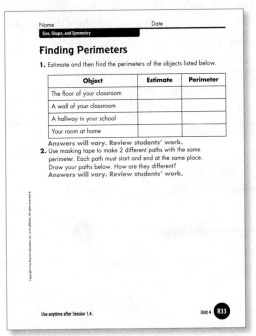

You have used tape to make a path 100 feet long. This path shows yards. How else is it different from the 100-foot path? Emphasize that the path starts and ends at the same place.

You have masking tape and a yardstick. You are going to make two different closed paths with the same perimeter. Your paths must be at least 25 yards long. What kinds of paths can you make?

Students might say:

 "We could make a square with 7 yards on each side. Then the path would be 28 yards in all."

Remember, you need to make two *different* paths with the same length. How can you plan the two paths?

Students might say:

 "We can make the first path any even number more than 25 yards. Then the second path can be a rectangle."

When students are finished, talk about the differences in the paths. Compare your two paths. How are they alike and different? How did you make them different?

Discuss the difference between a path in yards and a path in feet. How do you find the length of a path in feet if you know the number of yards? Why don't you need to measure the path again?

Distribute copies of Finding Perimeters (R33).

ELL **English Language Learners**

Provide a Word List Write the words *foot, yard, yardstick,* and *perimeter* on chart paper. Review the meaning of each word. Some English Language Learners may confuse *foot* with their foot (body part) and *yard* with property around their home, like their backyard.

Additional Resource

Student Math Handbook pages 104–105

Differentiation in Investigation 2

Mathematics in This Investigation

The mathematics focuses on describing and classifying polygons. The work also focuses on categorizing different quadrilaterals by attributes such as side length, angle size, and parallel sides.

Additional Resource: *Classification of Quadrilaterals,* page 155 (See Curriculum Unit 4)

Understanding the Mathematics

Students describe and sort different polygons. They explain how each is different and place each in its proper category. They use a strategic approach as they alter and combine polygons to make new polygons with ever increasing numbers of sides. They understand the relationship between squares and rectangles, which helps them sort quadrilaterals effectively. They describe and categorize the different quadrilaterals using such attributes as side length, angle size, and parallel sides.

Option: Assign the Extension activity.

Partially Understanding the Mathematics

Students describe the different polygons, but they may be limited in the details of their descriptions. They may not include important classifications when describing different polygons. Students may be able to alter and combine polygons to make new polygons, but they do not use a strategic approach to create a series of related shapes. Students may sometimes confuse the names of different shapes, such as squares and rectangles. They are still developing ways to describe the attributes of different quadrilaterals and may make mistakes in classifying those shapes correctly. They may recognize the different shapes, but they have difficulty determining some of the attributes or properties that differentiate the shapes.

Option: Assign the Practice activity.

Not Understanding the Mathematics

Students struggle with differentiating between the different polygons. They do not know how to distinguish between the polygons using such attributes as side length, angle size, and parallel sides. When describing the polygons, they incorrectly list the attributes of the shapes and are unclear about how the shapes differ. They have difficulty remembering all the names of the shapes and are only comfortable using a select few. They are not able to make new polygons by combining other polygons. They struggle to recognize the differences in the attributes of quadrilaterals and how such differences distinguish the quadrilaterals.

Option: Assign the Intervention activity.

Investigation 2 Quiz

In addition to your observations and students' work in Investigation 2, the Quiz (R34) can be used to gather more information.

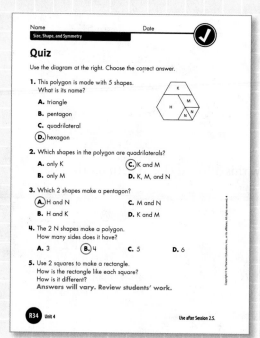

Intervention

30 MIN **PAIRS**

Sides of Polygons

Use anytime after Session 2.2.

Math Focus Points

◆ Combining polygons to make new polygons

◆ Recognizing number of sides as a descriptor of various polygons

Vocabulary: polygon, side

Materials: Power Polygons™ (A, C, E, G, L)

．．．．．．．．．．．．．．．．．．．．．．．．．．．．．．．．．．．．．

Tell students they will be using five of the Power Polygons to make new polygons. Provide each pair of students with the shapes A, C, E, G, and L.

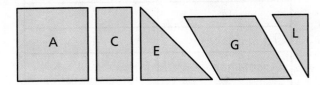

Which shape is a square? Which two shapes are triangles? Which shapes have 4 sides? Which shapes have 3 sides?

Display three combinations of the five shapes on an overhead or draw them on the board.

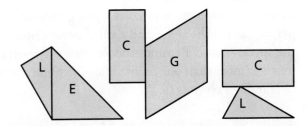

I have put pieces L and E together to make a new polygon. How many sides does it have? Point out that C and G also make a polygon, but C and L do not. Why do C and L not form a polygon when combined in this way?

Students might say:

"Shapes C and L don't make a new polygon. They touch at only one point. They show two polygons, not one."

Now use any two shapes to make a new polygon. Trace the outline of each shape to show the new polygon. Observe how students are joining the shapes and help them understand how the two shapes must join.

The straight edges of the polygon are the sides. How many sides does your new polygon have? Use an example such as the polygon made with shapes C and G in the figure. Model for students how to count the sides by touching each side as you move around the polygon.

Once students are comfortable using two shapes to make a new polygon, they can move on to using three different shapes or one shape and two copies of another shape.

Provide Sentence Stems Some English Language Learners may have difficulty verbalizing their responses. Help them by providing sentence stems. For example: Shapes _____ and _____ form a polygon because _____. It has _____ sides. Shapes _____ and _____ do not form a polygon because _____.

Additional Resource

Student Math Handbook pages 106–107

Practice

20 MIN · GROUPS

Naming Polygons

Use anytime after Session 2.3.

Math Focus Points

◆ Recognizing number of sides as a descriptor of various polygons

◆ Combining polygons to make new polygons

Vocabulary: side

Materials: Power Polygons, chart paper, R35

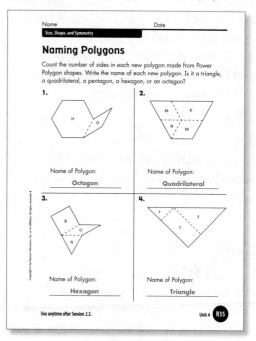

Display these two polygons on an overhead or draw them on the board.

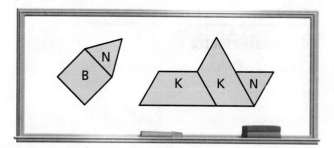

Remind students that they have been combining shapes in different ways to make new polygons. How many sides does each new polygon have?

Students might say:

 "The one with the square and the triangle is a pentagon. It has 5 sides, and anything with 5 sides is a pentagon."

 "The other one sort of looks like a hat. I don't know what name it should have, but I know there are 7 sides."

On chart paper, write the names for polygons with 3 to 8 sides to make a permanent chart for the classroom.

Name	Number of Sides
△ triangle	3
☐ quadrilateral	4
⬠ pentagon	5
⬡ hexagon	6
heptagon	7
octagon	8

Work with your group to make some polygons. Take turns. One person makes a polygon, another person counts the sides, and a third person finds the special name. Remind students that shapes must touch at more than one point. Then distribute copies of Naming Polygons (R35).

ELL · English Language Learners

Provide a Word List Have students write the name of each polygon shape in the table on an index card. On the back of each card, have students draw the shape and write the number of sides. Students can use these as flashcards to practice identifying shapes.

Additional Resource

Student Math Handbook pages 106–107

Extension

20 MIN GROUPS

Making New Polygons
Use anytime after Session 2.3.

Math Focus Points
◆ Recognizing number of sides as a descriptor of various polygons

◆ Combing polygons to make new polygons

Vocabulary: side

Materials: Power Polygons, R36

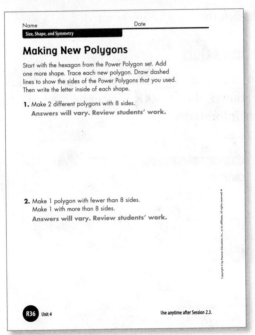

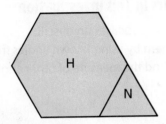

Students might say:

"Oh! Adding the little triangle made the number of sides go down. Now it has only 5 sides. I bet that won't happen very often."

Have students work with their groups to find new polygons that combine the hexagon with one other shape. They will be able to find polygons with 5 to 10 sides. Trace around your polygons to keep track of what you find.

Have students explore the various possibilities by asking the following questions. Are hexagons easier to find than octagons? Which kind of polygon is the easiest? Is there any way to make a quadrilateral?

Distribute copies of Making New Polygons (R36).

Remind students that they have been combining Power Polygons in different ways to make new polygons. Now imagine that you can use the hexagon and just one other shape. Will the new polygon always have more than 6 sides? What is the greatest number of sides it can have?

Give students a few minutes to try some different polygons. Ask if any students combined two polygons to make a pentagon. If so, have them share the new polygon. If not, display the polygon shown in the next column.

ELL **English Language Learners**

Provide a Word List Write the words *triangle, quadrilateral, pentagon, hexagon, heptagon,* and *octagon,* on chart paper. You may want to add to a permanent class chart for polygons if one has been started. Have students draw lines to divide a piece of paper into 6 equal sections. Next, have them write a word in each section. Then, ask them to draw a picture and list the number of sides and angles for each shape.

Additional Resource

Student Math Handbook pages 106–107

Differentiation in Investigation 3

Mathematics in This Investigation

The mathematics focuses on describing angles and measuring them by using known angles from Power Polygons to find the measure of other angles.

Understanding the Mathematics

Students understand that a right angle is 90 degrees and describe other angles as more than or less than 90 degrees. Using 90 degrees as a landmark, students see the relationships of other angles in Power Polygons. For example, they realize that if three of the same angles make a right angle, each of those angles has to be 30 degrees. Through reasoning, they determine which angles in the Power Polygon shapes are 30, 45, and 60 degrees, and use that information to find angles of 120 and 150 degrees.

Option: Assign the Extension activity.

Partially Understanding the Mathematics

Students are able to recognize right angles, but only in certain shapes where it is more obvious. They do not always correctly identify other angles as more than or less than 90 degrees. When using Power Polygons to find other angle measurements, students are able to create right angles, but they are uncertain how to use that information to determine angle size. For example, if they use two of the same angles to make a 90-degree angle, they don't necessarily realize that each angle is 45 degrees.

Option: Assign the Practice activity.

Not Understanding the Mathematics

Students struggle with recognizing right angles and do not yet understand that a right angle is 90 degrees. When looking at different angles and shapes, they are not able to determine if an angle is more than or less than 90 degrees. They have difficulty using Power Polygons to create right angles, and they do not understand how putting together different Power Polygons helps them to find the measure of angles.

Option: Assign the Intervention activity.

Investigation 3 Quiz

In addition to your observations and students' work in Investigation 3, the Quiz (R37) can be used to gather more information.

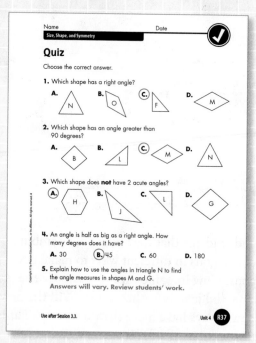

Intervention

25 MIN   PAIRS

Angle Sizes

Use anytime after Session 3.2.

Math Focus Points

◆ Measuring acute angles by relating them to 90 degrees

Vocabulary: angle, right angle, degree, acute

Materials: rulers, paper squares, Power Polygons

. . . .

Hold up two rulers at a right angle. These rulers make an angle. It is the same size as the corner of a paper square. It is called a right angle. It measures 90 degrees.

Make a right angle with your arms, one up and one to the right. Have students mimic you. Then have them find examples of right angles in the classroom.

Have students build a square with two of shape E, as shown to the right. Point to the right angle. How many degrees is each of these angles?

Students might say:

"I can fit two of the new angles into one right angle. A right angle is 90 degrees. So, half of a right angle is 45 degrees."

Hold up the two rulers again and make a 45-degree angle. Angles with measures of less than 90 degrees are called acute.

Have pairs use the Power Polygon triangles D, E, and F to make various right angles. At first, have students always put the right angle at the bottom left of the shape. After some practice, they can put the angle in any position in the shape.

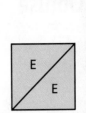  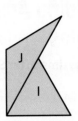

On an overhead, display Power Polygon shapes J, O, and L as shown above. Now I've made a right angle from three shapes, making three equal-sized angles. How many degrees are in each angle? Have a volunteer explain how they know each angle is 30 degrees.

Have students build a polygon with shapes I and J shown above. Point out the right angle. We just figured out this small angle in shape J is 30 degrees. So how many degrees is the angle in shape I? Help students recognize all angles in shape I are 60 degrees.

Conclude the activity by having students make right angles in three different ways: 45 + 45, 30 + 30 + 30, and 60 + 30.

(**ELL**) **English Language Learners**

Provide a Word List Write the words *angle, degrees,* and *right angle* on chart paper. Draw an angle. This is an angle. *Angles* come in many sizes. *Degrees* are used to measure *angles*. Draw a right angle. If an angle makes a *square* corner, it is called a *right angle*. Right angles *measure 90 degrees*. Have students find examples of 90-degree angles in the classroom.

Additional Resource

Student Math Handbook pages 111–113

Practice

20 MIN   GROUPS

Building Acute and Obtuse Angles

Use anytime after Session 3.2.

Math Focus Points

◆ Measuring acute angles by relating them to 90 degrees

Vocabulary: acute, obtuse

Materials: rulers, Power Polygons, blank paper (1 sheet per group), R38

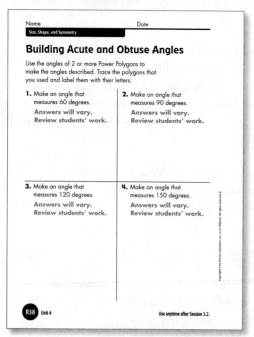

Hold up two rulers at a right angle. How can I make this angle smaller? How can I make it larger? Have volunteers show you how to change the rulers or have students demonstrate using their arms. The size of the angle is the amount of the opening, not the length of the sides.

You can use Power Polygons to make angles of different sizes. Remember, acute angles are *smaller* than a right angle. Obtuse angles are *larger* than a right angle.

Distribute Power Polygons and paper to each group. Show students how to use the Power Polygons to make one acute angle and one obtuse angle. Have students lay the shapes on the corners of their paper to show whether the angles are bigger or smaller than a right angle.

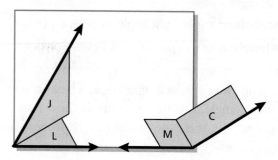

Have students sort the Power Polygon triangles. Which triangle has an obtuse angle? What is the degree measure of the angle?

Have students sort the Power Polygons into shapes with obtuse angles and shapes without. Then have them use known angles to find degree measures of each obtuse angle. If students are uncertain about finding angles, refer to Session 3.1, p.92.

Distribute copies of Building Acute and Obtuse Angles (R38).

ELL **English Language Learners**

Model Thinking Aloud Some students may confuse *acute* and *obtuse*. Demonstrate these angles as you model your thinking aloud. Hold up two rulers at a right angle. I know that a right angle is the same as a square corner. It measures 90 degrees. I can compare other angles to a square corner. Move the ruler to form an obtuse angle. This angle is *larger* than a right angle so it is *obtuse*. Move the rulers to form an acute angle. This angle is *smaller* than a right angle so it is *acute*.

Additional Resource

Student Math Handbook page 112

Extension

 20 MIN GROUPS

Finding Equal Angles
Use anytime after Session 3.1.

Math Focus Points
◆ Identifying a right angle as 90 degrees
◆ Measuring acute angles by relating them to 90 degrees

Vocabulary: right angle, angle, degree

Materials: Power Polygons, R39

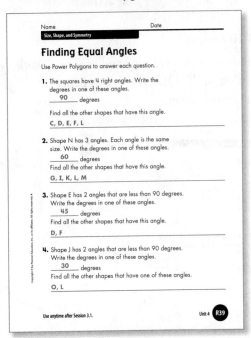

Display these figures on an overhead.

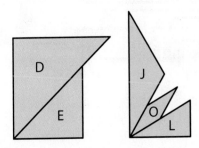

I used Power Polygons to make some right angles. I used two of the same angle to make the first right angle. What does that tell you about the size of each angle?

Students might say:

"The little angles in D and E must each be 45 degrees. 45 + 45 = 90."

Repeat for the second figure with three equal angles. Then display Power Polygons I and N.

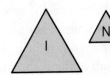

How do you know when two angles are equal? Are the angles in these triangles equal? How do you know? Emphasize that the size of an angle is the amount of the opening, not the length of the sides. Allow students time to discover that they can place one shape on top of another to check for equal angles.

How many degrees does each angle in shape I measure?

Students might say:

"I see shapes I and J make a right angle, too. I know the little angle in J is 30 degrees. So, each angle in I must be 60 degrees."

Can you find other Power Polygons with this angle? Does a shape need to be a triangle to have this angle? Have students work together to find all the 60-degree angles in the Power Polygon set.

Distribute copies of Finding Equal Angles (R39).

ELL English Language Learners

Rephrase If students have difficulty finding equal angles, rephrase the question. How do you know when angles are the *same* size? Are the angles in the triangle the *same* size?

Additional Resource
Student Math Handbook pages 111–113

Differentiation in Investigation 4

Mathematics in This Investigation

The mathematics focuses on finding and understanding area. The area of different polygons is determined by decomposing shapes and using symmetry.

Understanding the Mathematics

Students determine the area of different polygons accurately using square units. They are able to use the symmetry of the polygons to help them find the area by focusing on half of the shape and doubling it. They can also decompose a shape into smaller, more familiar shapes. They find the area of those smaller shapes and add the areas together to determine the area of the original shape. Some students may also be able to find the area using another unit of measurement, such as a hexagon, trapezoid, parallelogram, or triangle. Some students can build more complex shapes and find their area.

Option: Assign the Extension activity.

Partially Understanding the Mathematics

Students have some difficulty finding the area of different polygons using square units. They have a general understanding of symmetry, but struggle to understand how symmetry can be used to find the area of a shape. When finding area, students are most comfortable decomposing shapes into square units and counting each unit by ones until they have counted all the units and have determined the area.

Option: Assign the Practice activity.

Not Understanding the Mathematics

Students do not understand how to determine the area of different shapes and may confuse area with perimeter or another form of measurement. They do not yet understand the concept of symmetry and how it can be used to find area. They struggle with using square units to find area, particularly in non-rectangular shapes. They are unable to decompose shapes into smaller shapes to find the area.

Option: Assign the Intervention activity.

Investigation 4 Quiz

In addition to your observations and students' work in Investigation 4, the Quiz (R40) can be used to gather more information.

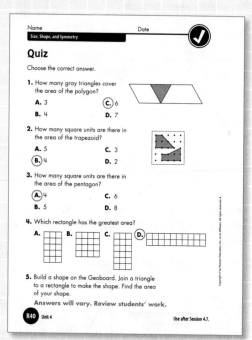

Intervention

25 MIN **PAIRS**

Geoboard Areas

Use anytime after Session 4.4.

Math Focus Points

◆ Finding the area of polygons using square units

◆ Finding the area of polygons by decomposing shapes

Vocabulary: square unit

Materials: Geoboards, rubber bands, T51

. . . .

Have students make some squares and rectangles on their Geoboards. How can we compare the sizes of these shapes? How can you tell how much of the Geoboard each shape covers?

Remind students that *area* is the amount of space a flat object covers. Today we'll use square units to measure area. How many square units are there in each shape you made?

Model how to put rubber bands around individual square units. Start with the top rectangle shown on the left Geoboard below. Make a rectangle like this. Now put one rubber band around each little square. How many square units are there in the rectangle?

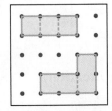 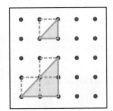

Next, have students make the hexagon illustrated on the left Geoboard. Students put rubber bands around each square unit to find the area. Model how to decompose the figure into two rectangles. What is the area of each rectangle? How can you use this to find the area of the whole shape?

After students have worked with shapes composed of squares and rectangles, introduce the triangles on the

right Geoboard. Make one square unit, then use a rubber band to divide the square in half. Ask students what the area of 1 triangle is. Help them recognize that it is $\frac{1}{2}$. Build the second shape. What is its area?

Use Geoboard Dot Paper (T51) to draw the diagrams below. Have students create each figure and find the area. How can you add more than one area to find the total? Are there different ways to do this? Encourage pairs to decompose shapes in different ways to check that they always get the same area.

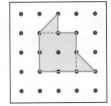 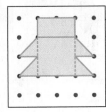

ELL **English Language Learners**

Model Thinking Aloud Students may need help seeing how square units describe the areas of triangles. Use a triangle that is one half of a 2 × 2 square. I can cut a square in half to get two triangles. Each triangle is one half of a square unit. I can fit the square onto the shape and measure its area that way.

Additional Resource

Student Math Handbook page 115

Practice

20 MIN **PAIRS**

Find the Area

Use anytime after Session 4.6.

Math Focus Points

◆ Find the area of polygons by decomposing shapes

Materials: T2, M2 (from Unit 1), R41

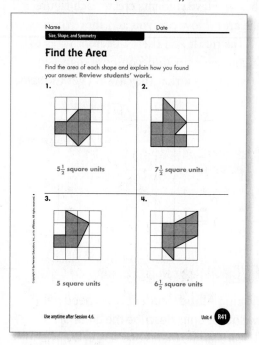

You've been using Geoboards to find areas in square units. The squares on grid paper are just like the squares on a Geoboard. Show the following shapes on the transparency for One-Centimeter Grid Paper (T2). Then have students draw these shapes on One-Centimeter Grid Paper (M2).

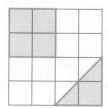

What is the area of the square? What is the area of the triangle? How does the area of the right triangle compare to the area of the square?

Remind students of their work with Geoboards. A rectangle can be cut in half diagonally to make 2 equal triangles. The area of the triangle is $\frac{1}{2}$ the area of the rectangle. Show the following shape on T2, then have students draw the shape on M2.

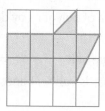

Ask students to find the area of the shape. After a few minutes ask for solutions.

Students might say:

 "I broke the shape into 3 parts. The rectangle is 6 square units. Then there is $\frac{1}{2}$ of a square. The other triangle is $\frac{1}{2}$ of a 2-square-unit rectangle, so it's 1. The area is 7 and $\frac{1}{2}$ square units."

Repeat the activity with the shape below.

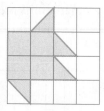

Distribute copies of Find the Area (R41).

(**ELL**) **English Language Learners**

Partner Talk Have students describe how to find the area of a polygon to a partner. Encourage students to use the words *area* and *square units* as they point to the parts of the polygon.

Additional Resource

Student Math Handbook page 115

30 MIN GROUPS

Extension

Polygon Areas

Use anytime after Session 4.4.

Math Focus Points

◆ Finding the area of polygons using square units

◆ Finding the area of polygons by decomposing shapes

Vocabulary: square unit, pentagon

Materials: Geoboards, rubber bands, T51, R42

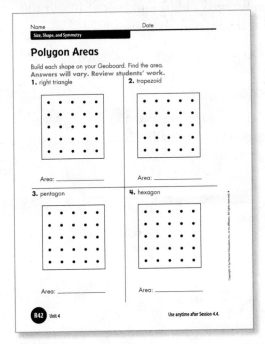

Display these polygons on Geoboard Dot Paper (T51).

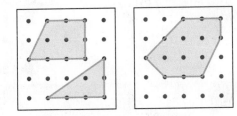

You have been finding areas of polygons by breaking them into rectangles and triangles. How can you find the areas of these shapes? Encourage

students to find more than one way to find each area. You may need to spend time helping students determine that the right triangle is half of a 2 × 3 rectangle.

Now you're going to build shapes of your own. A right triangle joined to one side of a square or rectangle makes a trapezoid. Have students build trapezoids and find the areas of their shapes. Who can build a trapezoid with an area of 9 square units?

Students might say:

"I can build a 2 × 4 rectangle and add a 1-unit triangle to the end. It looks like the trapezoid with 5 square units. But it's 2 squares wider."

Next have students build pentagons and hexagons and find their areas. How do you know if your shape is a pentagon? A hexagon? How can you check?

Students might say:

"I know a hexagon has to have 6 sides, so I just need to count the sides."

Last, have the students in each group compete to make complex, irregular polygons. Once the shapes are finished, the group should work together to find the areas of all their shapes.

Distribute copies of Polygon Areas (R42).

ELL English Language Learners

Rephrase Remind students that *area* measures the amount of space an object covers. If needed, rephrase questions. For example: Who can build a trapezoid that covers 9 square units?

Additional Resource

Student Math Handbook page 115

Differentiation in Investigation 1

Mathematics in This Investigation

The mathematics focuses on place-value concepts up to 1,000 as well as adding and subtracting multiples of 10 and 100.

Additional Resource: *Creating a Supportive Environment for Hedson*, pages 87–89 (See *Implementing Investigations in Grade 4*)

Understanding the Mathematics

Students locate numbers to 1,000 efficiently using their 1,000 books. They recognize the place value of digits in larger numbers. As they cross hundreds when they are locating numbers, students can explain how the hundreds digit changes (e.g., 298 + 4 = 302). Students add and subtract multiples of 10 and 100 easily. They understand how to solve problems with numbers up to 1,000 and use multiples of 10 and 100 to help them find the answer.

Option: Assign the Extension activity.

Partially Understanding the Mathematics

Students may have some difficulty finding numbers in their 1,000 books. They understand the place value of numbers to 1,000, but struggle crossing the hundreds as they locate numbers. They add and subtract multiples of 10 and 100, but are less organized. Students may not understand how using multiples of 10 and 100 are efficient ways for finding a solution. They may make small errors in their calculations when solving problems.

Option: Assign the Practice activity.

Not Understanding the Mathematics

Students are not able to locate many of the numbers in their 1,000 books. They have difficulty understanding the place value of digits and struggle crossing the hundreds when they try to locate a number. When solving addition and subtraction problems in the hundreds, students may be most comfortable counting by 1s or by multiples of numbers other than 10 or 100. They are less organized in their work and are unable to make the connection between adding multiples of 10 and 100 with adding numbers up to 1,000.

Option: Assign the Intervention activity.

Investigation 1 Quiz

In addition to your observations and students' work in Investigation 1, the Quiz (R43) can be used to gather more information.

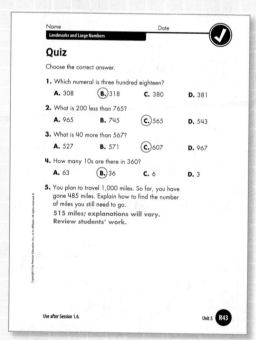

Intervention

20 MIN   GROUPS

Adding and Subtracting 1s, 10s, and 100s

Use anytime after Session 1.3.

Math Focus Points

◆ Adding and subtracting multiples of 10, 100, and 1,000

◆ Reading, writing, and sequencing numbers to 1,000

Materials: 1,000 books (from Session 1.1), R44

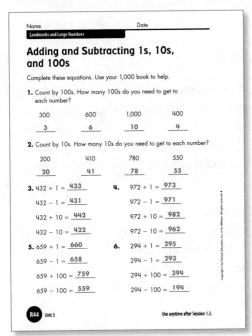

Each of you have made a 1,000 book. Let's use your books to do some counting. How many 100s do you count to get to 400? How do you know? Have students turn the pages of the 1,000 books as they count. Now we'll count by 10s up to 410. Do you need to count every ten? What other counting strategies can you use? Have students share different ways to count to 410 using the 1,000 books.

Next, have a volunteer with closed eyes randomly point to a square in his or her 1,000 book, for example, the square with 483. How can we find out what number goes in this square? How do you know it must be greater than [401] and less than

[500]? What landmark numbers is it close to? Once the number is identified, have all students write it in their 1,000 books.

Our number has 3 digits. What are they? Each digit has a place. What are the names of the places? Draw a place-value chart on the board, writing the digits of the randomly chosen number in each respective column. Use the chart to review the terms *digit* and *place*.

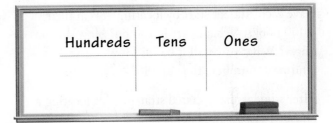

What place changes if you add 1 to our number? Subtract 1? Repeat the discussion for adding and subtracting 10 and then for adding and subtracting 100.

Distribute copies of Adding and Subtracting 1s, 10s, and 100s (R44).

Students might say:

"When you add and subtract 10s, it changes the 10s digit. When you add and subtract 100s, it changes the 100s digit."

Provide a Word List Write the words *place, place value, digit, ones, tens,* and *hundreds* on chart paper. Review the meanings, then help students write or draw examples for each.

Additional Resource

Student Math Handbook page 6

Practice

30 MIN · PAIRS

More Changing Places
Use anytime after Session 1.5.

Math Focus Points

◆ Adding and subtracting multiples of 10, 100, and 1,000

Materials: 1,000 books (from Session 1.1), Change Cards (1 deck per pair), Digit Cards

Have each student start by locating 486 in their 1,000 books. What chart is 486 on? How do you know? What row will it be in? How can you use landmark numbers to find 486?

After students have shared strategies for locating a number, display the Change Card −50. Let's imagine you were playing *Changing Places* and drew this card. If you make this change to 486, will you get a number in the 400s? What digit in 486 changes? How do you know?

Ask students to solve 486 − 50 using their 1,000 books. Draw this table on the board to record the change you just made.

Start	Change	End
486	−50	436

Do another problem, 318 + 200, in which the hundreds place changes. Continue the activity with a problem where the number changes in two places - 581 and the Change Card +40. When you make this change, more than one place changes. Which place stays the same? How do you know?

Students might say:

"We're adding 4 tens, so the tens digit will change. But, 4 tens + 8 tens = 12 tens, so the hundreds digit also changes."

"If I start in my 1,000 book on 581 and count 4 rows, I end on a new page. The ending number will have a 6 in the hundreds place, not 5."

Repeat with another example, such as 712 and the Change Card −20. As you work through the examples, emphasize first thinking about the values of the digits rather than immediately beginning to count on or back.

Provide pairs of students with Change Cards. Ask a volunteer to suggest a starting number. Then his or her partner draws a Change Card. Before you make a change, talk about what places in the number will change. Then count rows or pages to make the change.

Watch to check that students know to count the rows when adding and subtracting 10s and to count the pages when adding and subtracting 100s. Continue the activity with partners taking turns suggesting starting numbers and drawing Change Cards.

⬤ **ELL** ⬤ **English Language Learners**

Partner Talk Have students work in pairs to practice reading and writing 3-digit numbers. Provide each pair with Digit Cards. The more proficient speaker picks 3 digits and makes a "secret" number. He or she reads the number aloud; the partner writes it as a numeral. Have partners switch roles if they are able.

Additional Resource

Student Math Handbook

Game: *Changing Places* SMH G2
Materials: 1,000 books, Change Cards

Extension

25 MIN   PAIRS

Using the 1,000 Book

Use anytime after Session 1.1.

Math Focus Points

◆ Reading, writing, and sequencing numbers to 1,000

Materials: 1,000 books (from Session 1.1), Digit Cards, bag, R45

Name _____ Date _____

Landmarks and Large Numbers

Using the 1,000 Book

Write each number in your 1,000 book. Then write the chart on which the number belongs. Use the last number on a chart to name it.

1. 375 is on the __400__ chart. 2. 962 is on the __1,000__ chart.

3. 71 is on the __100__ chart. 4. 522 is on the __600__ chart.

5. 804 is on the __900__ chart. 6. 298 is on the __300__ chart.

Choose 2 numbers on each chart. Tell how to find the difference between your 2 numbers. *Answers will vary for Problems 7–8. Review students' work.*

7. _____ and _____ are on the 700 chart.

I found the difference by _____

_____

8. _____ and _____ are on the 400 chart.

I found the difference by _____

_____

Use anytime after Session 1.1. Unit 5 **R45**

Each of you have made a 1,000 book. Each page has one 100 chart. How many charts does your book have? What is the last number on each chart? Where is it? What is the first number on each chart? Where is it?

Emphasize that a chart is named according to the last number on it, the number in the bottom right corner. What are the numbers on the 300 chart? The 800 chart? What is the name of the first chart in your book? The last chart?

Remind students that they have written enough numbers on each chart so that they can locate *any* number less than 1,000 in their books. Have volunteers explain how they decided which numbers to write on their charts. During this unit you will

be writing more numbers in your 1,000 books. Let's do an example now. Put a deck of Digit Cards in a bag. Have a student draw three cards to generate a random 3-digit number.

Have students locate this number in their 1,000 books, writing it in the correct square. What strategies did you use to locate the number in your book? Did you use some landmark numbers? Which ones?

Students might say:

"I know the number [564] is between [501] and [600], so it goes on the [600] chart."

"I used [570] as a landmark. Our number is in that row, so I counted back from [570] to [564]."

After students have shared their strategies, repeat with a few more random 3-digit numbers. Next, have each pair turn to the same chart in their 1,000 books. Each of you should secretly choose a number from the chart. Tell each other what number you chose, and find the difference between your two numbers. Encourage various strategies, such as adding up, subtracting back, and using landmark numbers.

Distribute copies of Using the 1,000 Book (R45).

ELL **English Language Learners**

Rephrase Help students understand *landmark number* by comparing it to a geographical landmark. *When I go on a driving trip, a landmark is a place I may stop and visit. Landmark numbers are stopping places you use when counting, adding, and subtracting.*

Additional Resource

Student Math Handbook pages 13–15

Differentiation in Investigation 2

Mathematics in This Investigation

The mathematics focuses on solving whole-number addition problems accurately and efficiently and analyzing and comparing addition strategies.

Additional Resource: *Describing, Comparing, and Classifying Addition Strategies,* page 173 (See Curriculum Unit 5)

Understanding the Mathematics

Students solve addition problems accurately, efficiently, and flexibly, and they use clear and concise notation. When given the start to a problem, they are able to use that information to help them solve the rest of the problem. Students solve addition problems with 3- and 4-digit numbers using different strategies. They compare strategies and can effectively use any of the strategies for solving addition problems. Students combine large chunks of numbers when adding and use a minimum number of steps to reach their answer.

Option: Assign the Extension activity.

Partially Understanding the Mathematics

Students solve addition problems accurately, but may not be efficient. They are able to solve problems given the start, but may not recognize the relationship between the start they just solved and the related problem. Students solve problems with 3- and 4- digit numbers using one strategy they are most comfortable with. They often break numbers apart into many chunks, making it more difficult to keep track of their work and accurately solve the problem.

Option: Assign the Practice activity.

Not Understanding the Mathematics

Students have difficulty solving addition problems. These students may not make the connection between a given start and how it's related to solving the problem. They may also have difficulty with 3- and 4-digit numbers and may only feel comfortable with smaller numbers. Students are not yet comfortable using any of the addition strategies. They may lose track of the values of the digits in the problem, producing an incorrect answer.

Option: Assign the Intervention activity.

Investigation 2 Quiz

In addition to your observations and students' work in Investigation 2, the Quiz (R46) can be used to gather more information.

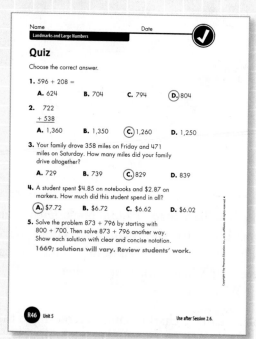

Intervention

30 MIN   PAIRS

Reviewing Addition

Use anytime after Session 2.1.

Math Focus Points

◆ Adding 3- and 4-digit numbers

Vocabulary: addition strategies

Materials: R47

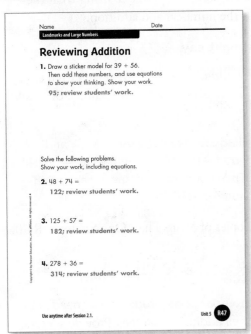

Tell students you will be talking about addition strategies they learned in previous grades. Tonya and her dad drove 58 miles to her grandma's house. Then they drove 87 miles home. How many miles did they drive in all?

Discuss the problem until students seem to understand the given information. Use questions such as the following:

◆ Is it going to be more or less than 100? More or less than 200? How do you know?

Students should understand that the sum should be between 100 and 200.

Write the problem 58 + 87 on the board. This is the problem we need to solve. Remember how you used stickers in 3rd grade? Let's sketch these numbers.

As you begin, ask students how many 10s you should draw for 58, and how many 1s. Repeat for 87.

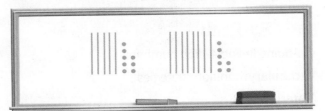

Add these numbers, and use equations to show your thinking.

Students might say:

"First I did 50 + 50 = 100. I still had three strips, so 100 + 30 = 130. Then I counted the singles and there were 15. 130 + 15 = 145."

Encourage students to think about becoming more efficient. I see [Amelia] added by place. Could she add the 50 and 80 all at once? Could you add 7 + 8 without counting by ones?

Ask if students solved 58 + 87 another way. Discuss solutions again, encouraging students to think about efficiency.

Distribute copies of Reviewing Addition (R47). You may want to work through Problem 1 together as another example. Students will solve the problems in different ways. Have volunteers present their different solutions.

ELL English Language Learners

Partner Talk Have students work in pairs. Have more proficient speakers explain how to use the sticker models to add while the other partner models with the strips and singles. Encourage students to use the words *place*, *place value*, *digit*, *tens*, and *ones* in their explanations.

Additional Resource

Student Math Handbook pages 8–9

Practice

20 MIN **INDIVIDUALS**

More Than One Strategy

Use anytime after Session 2.2.

Math Focus Points

◆ Adding 3- and 4-digit numbers

Vocabulary: addition strategies

Materials: R48

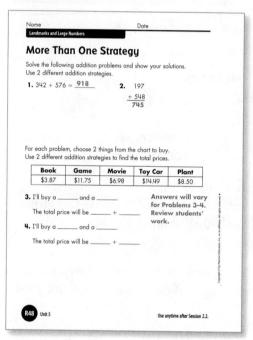

Name _____ Date _____

Landmarks and Large Numbers

More Than One Strategy

Solve the following addition problems and show your solutions.
Use 2 different addition strategies.

1. 342 + 576 = __918__   2. 197
                              + 548
                              ‾‾‾‾‾
                               745

For each problem, choose 2 things from the chart to buy.
Use 2 different addition strategies to find the total prices.

Book	Game	Movie	Toy Car	Plant
$3.87	$11.75	$6.98	$14.49	$8.50

3. I'll buy a _____ and a _____.   Answers will vary
                                      for Problems 3–4.
   The total price will be ___ + ___. Review students'
                                      work.
4. I'll buy a _____ and a _____.

   The total price will be ___ + ___.

R48 Unit 5   Use anytime after Session 2.2.

. . . .

It's good to know more than one addition strategy. The numbers in a problem may work better with one strategy than another. Let's review our addition strategies. Refer to the class strategy charts you have previously made. Have students use these charts to help them describe examples of different strategies.

Read the following problem aloud. You bought a plant and a book of poetry for your mom for her birthday. You paid $5.49 for the plant and $3.97 for the book of poetry. Write the items and prices on the board. What problem are we solving? After students respond, write the equation on the board.

plant $5.49
poetry book $3.97

$5.49 + $3.97 =

Ask students to solve the problem, using what they know about the numbers and addition.

Students might say:

"I added by place - starting with the dollars. I got $8, $1.30 and $0.16 and added them."

"I added 3 cents to the book and got $4.00. $5.49 + $4.00 = $9.49. Then I subtracted the 3 cents and got $9.46."

Distribute copies of More Than One Strategy (R48).

(**ELL**) English Language Learners

Provide Sentence Stems Students may need help explaining their addition strategies. Provide sentence stems such as the following:

◆ To add by breaking apart one number, I can use the parts _____.

◆ If I add 3 cents to this price, I need to subtract _____.

Additional Resource

Student Math Handbook
Game: *Close to 1,000* SMH G3
Materials: Digit Cards, M22

20 MIN **PAIRS**

Extension

Aim for Zero

Use anytime after Session 2.5.

Math Focus Points

◆ Finding combinations of 3-digit numbers that add to 1,000

Materials: Digit Cards (1 deck per pair), M21 (1 per pair), M22 (2 per pair)

. . . .

Distribute the Digit Cards, the rules for *Close to 1,000* (M21), and *Close to 1,000* Recording Sheets (M22) to each pair.

Students have already played this game, so discuss some of the strategies they discovered. Ask questions such as the following but encourage all student-created game strategies:

◆ Do you start with the hundreds place first? Or, do you make a number and then find out how far from 1,000 you are?

◆ If you can make 900 with the hundreds, what do you try to do with the tens and ones?

In the game you've been playing, the player with the lowest score wins. We're going to make two changes in the rules.

1. For each round, record your score with a plus sign or a minus sign to show whether your total is more or less than 1,000.

2. The final score closest to zero wins.

Have students read the scoring variation at the bottom of the rule sheet and ask if there are any questions about this variation. Play two rounds with the whole class so students can begin to learn the variation.

Have students begin playing in pairs. Circulate to check that they are keeping score correctly in the scores for the individual rounds and that they are keeping track of their overall score. For example, in Round 1 if the score is +5, for the next round students should try to get close to 995, not 1,000.

After students have played the game for a while, discuss how the variation changes their game strategies. In the regular game, getting a big score like 30 for a round would be really bad. Why is this not so bad for this variation of the game? Students should realize that if they are over by 30, in the next round(s) they want to be below 1,000 by 30.

ELL **English Language Learners**

Model Thinking Aloud Students may notice that the word *strategy* is used in two ways. Explain how the word can be used to describe different situations, but mean the same thing.

The word *strategy* is used here in two different ways. I use an *addition strategy* to add numbers. I use a *game strategy* to choose the numbers in *Close to 1,000*. So, the word *strategy* doesn't just apply to addition. It can be any plan I create to reach a goal.

Additional Resource

Student Math Handbook pages 8–9

Differentiation in Investigation 3

Mathematics in This Investigation

The mathematics focuses on place-value concepts up to 10,000 as well as adding and subtracting multiples of 10, 100 and 1,000.

Understanding the Mathematics

Working with the 10,000 chart, students understand what happens when a number crosses a thousand, and they can locate numbers quickly on the 10,000 chart. They add and subtract accurately and efficiently with numbers in the 1,000s. Students understand the place value of large numbers and add and subtract a sequence of numbers using multiples of 10, 100, and 1,000.

Option: Assign the Extension activity.

Partially Understanding the Mathematics

Students add and subtract numbers in the 1,000s, but are less efficient. They understand the place value and the increasing values of the numbers, but may encounter errors in their calculations. They may not use the multiples of 10, 100, and 1,000 to solve addition and subtraction problems, but instead continue to use a strategy with which they are comfortable. These students may have difficulty going from 3-digit to 4-digit numbers, but are still able to determine the size of the numbers.

Option: Assign the Practice activity.

Not Understanding the Mathematics

Students are not accurate when adding and subtracting large numbers in the 1,000s. They may be overwhelmed with the size of the numbers and may struggle with finding accurate solutions to the problems. They do not have a strong concept of place value and often get the values of the numbers mixed up when computing. They are still struggling to learn addition strategies and do not see how adding and subtracting by multiples of 10, 100, and 1,000 will help to solve these problems. When crossing into the hundreds and thousands, they may often misrepresent the values of the different digits, resulting in incorrect answers.

Option: Assign the Intervention activity.

Investigation 3 Quiz

In addition to your observations and students' work in Investigation 3, the Quiz (R49) can be used to gather more information.

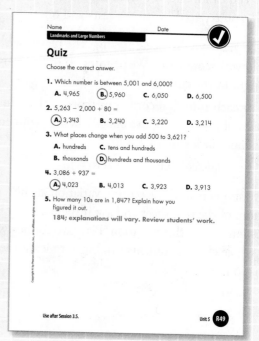

20 MIN   **PAIRS**

Intervention

How Many 10s Are in 1,000?
Use anytime after Session 3.2.

Math Focus Points

◆ Understanding the structure of 10,000 and its equivalence to one thousand 10s, one hundred 100s, and ten 1,000s

Materials: 1,000 books (from Session 1.1)

Revisit the sticker place-value model from Grade 3. The sticker representation includes single stickers, strips of 10 stickers, and sheets of 100 stickers.

If you could fill up your 1,000 book with stickers, that would be lots and lots of stickers. Let's look at the first page of your book. How many 10-strips will fit on just this page? If necessary, have students point to the end of each row as they count by 10s. A visual representation in which alternate rows are shaded may help students better keep track of the counting.

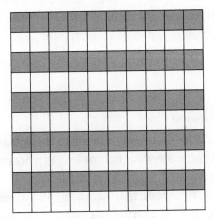

There are 10 strips on this first page of your book. This page is a 100 chart. So, how many 10s equal 100?

We have found the number of 10s in 100. How can we find the number of 10s in 153? Encourage students to continue using their 1000s book.

Students might say:

 "I can keep counting the rows of 10 until I get to the row that ends with 150. It's 15!"

Repeat this discussion with a few more numbers, such as 278, 316, and 465. Encourage students to think of each 100 as ten 10s.

ELL   English Language Learners

Provide Sentence Stems Write the following sentence stem on the board to help students clearly communicate the number of 10s in a number.

There are _____ 10s in _____.

Additional Resource
Student Math Handbook page 6

Practice

20 MIN **PAIRS**

What Places Change?

Use anytime after Session 3.4.

Math Focus Points

◆ Adding and subtracting multiples of 10, 100, and 1,000

Materials: Change Cards (1 deck per pair), R50

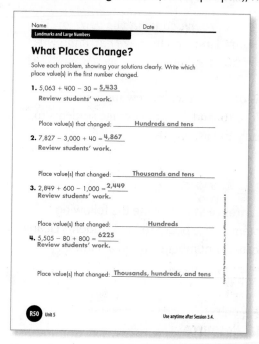

Name _____ Date _____

Landmarks and Large Numbers

What Places Change?

Solve each problem, showing your solutions clearly. Write which place value(s) in the first number changed.

1. 5,063 + 400 − 30 = 5,433
Review students' work.

Place value(s) that changed: ___Hundreds and tens___

2. 7,827 − 3,000 + 40 = 4,867
Review students' work.

Place value(s) that changed: ___Thousands and tens___

3. 2,849 + 600 − 1,000 = 2,449
Review students' work.

Place value(s) that changed: ___Hundreds___

4. 5,505 − 80 + 800 = 6225
Review students' work.

Place value(s) that changed: _Thousands, hundreds, and tens_

R50 Unit 5 | Use anytime after Session 3.4.

. . . .

Distribute Change Cards to each pair. Review the meaning of *multiple,* and then have them find multiples of 10, 100, and 1,000 on the Change Cards.

Students might say:

"A multiple of 10 ends in 1 zero. A multiple of 100 ends in 2 zeros. A multiple of 1,000 ends in 3 zeros."

"A multiple of 1,000 is also a multiple of 100 and 10."

Ask four students to each suggest a digit from 1 to 9. What 4-digit numbers can we make from these digits? Which 4-digit number is the greatest? Who can locate this number on our class 10,000 chart?

Write the greatest of these student-generated numbers on the board.

Have students in each pair draw 2 Change Cards. Write the equation that shows your starting number and your 2 changes. Solve the problem to find the new number.

Point out that students can do the 2 changes in either order. Have pairs try this to see that they get the same sum. Was one change easier to do than the other? Will you always do the easier change first?

Allow time for pairs to find the new number. How did the number change? Did more than 1 digit change? Why do you think so?

Encourage students to focus on the digits rather than simply counting on. If I add a multiple of 100, what place will change for sure? What other place might also change? When does this happen?

Distribute copies of What Places Change? (R50).

(**ELL**) **English Language Learners**

Rephrase Use place-value charts to check that students know the word names for the places in 4-digit numbers. If I start from the left, the places are *thousands, hundreds, tens,* and *ones.* What are the word names if I start from the right?

Additional Resource

Student Math Handbook pages 6–7

Extension

25 MIN · GROUPS

More Road Trips

Use anytime after Session 3.4.

Math Focus Points

◆ Adding 3- and 4-digit numbers

Materials: M26, R51

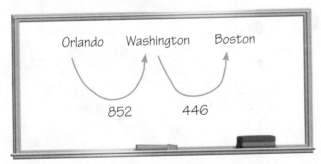

Name _____ Date _____
Landmarks and Large Numbers

More Road Trips
Use the driving distance table on page 46 of the
Student Activity Book. Write where you start, end,
and the cities you visit. Find the total miles. Show
your solution on the back of this sheet.

Answers will vary. Review
students' work.

1. Use 3 cities. Plan a trip close to 3,000 miles.

Cities: _____

Total Miles: _____

2. Use 3 cities. Plan a trip between 3,000 and 4,000 miles.

Cities: _____

Total Miles: _____

3. Use 4 cities. Plan a trip shorter than 4,000 miles.

Cities: _____

Total Miles: _____

4. Use 5 cities. Plan a trip close to 5,000 miles.

Cities: _____

Total Miles: _____

Use anytime after Session 3.4.   Unit 5 **R51**

Students have been using City to City: How Many
Miles? (M26) to plan road trips. Today you will
plan trips that have a certain number of miles as
the goal. Let's start with a 3-city trip that must be
more than 1,500 miles, but shorter than 2,000
miles. Write the following on the board.

Students might say:

"It won't work. It's less than 1,500
miles. 900 + 500 = 1,400 and the
actual answer is even less than that."

Now plan a trip with 4 cities that is more than
4,500 miles, but less than 6,000 miles. Give
students a few minutes to solve the problem and
share solutions with a partner.

Draw this diagram on the board to show one
possible solution.

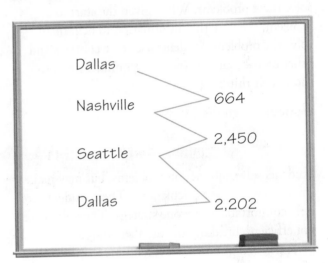

Make a quick estimate. Does it seem like this sum
will be between 4,500 and 6,000? Students can
explain how they added the numbers.

Distribute copies of More Road Trips (R51).

ELL · English Language Learners

Partner Talk Students work in pairs. Have the more
proficient speaker explain how they planned their city
trips while the partner points to the city distances
listed on M26.

Additional Resource

Student Math Handbook pages 8–9

Would this trip work? How do you know? Give
students a brief amount of time to think, and then
ask for an answer.

Differentiation in Investigation 4

Mathematics in This Investigation

The mathematics focuses on solving subtraction problems accurately and efficiently and on representing subtraction situations in different ways.

Additional Resource: *Subtraction Strategies,* pages 183–185 (See Curriculum Unit 5)

Understanding the Mathematics

Students solve subtraction problems with numbers in the 1,000s accurately and efficiently. They are comfortable using different subtraction strategies to solve these problems. When given the start to a problem, they use that information to help them solve the problem. Students use story contexts and other representations, including number lines, to show their thinking.

Option: Assign the Extension activity.

Partially Understanding the Mathematics

Students solve subtraction problems, but may make small errors in their calculations. These students are only comfortable using one strategy. They often are not efficient, breaking the numbers into too many pieces. When given the start for a problem, students often solve it and the problem correctly, but they do not see the relationship between the start of the problem and its solution. Students use story contexts and other representations like number lines to help them understand and solve subtraction problems.

Option: Assign the Practice activity.

Not Understanding the Mathematics

Students have difficulty solving subtraction problems with numbers in the 1,000s. Their solutions are generally incorrect and less efficient. They attempt to solve subtraction problems using only one strategy, a strategy that doesn't always result in a correct answer. When given the start for a problem, students struggle to relate the start to the overall problem. They do not make clear representations to help solve subtraction problems accurately.

Option: Assign the Intervention activity.

Investigation 4 Quiz

In addition to your observations and students' work in Investigation 4, the Quiz (R52) can be used to gather more information.

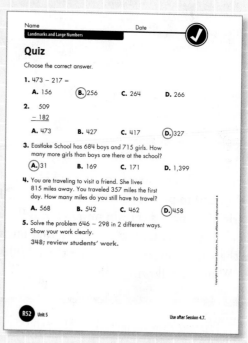

Intervention

30 MIN   **PAIRS**

Strategies with Larger Numbers
Use anytime after Session 4.5.

Math Focus Points
◆ Solving subtraction problems by breaking numbers apart

Vocabulary: subtraction strategies

Students may need extra instruction to extend their subtraction strategies to the 4-digit numbers in the activity Which Is Farther? How Much Farther? (page 156). Write this simpler problem on the board.

> In the first week, 85 adults and 63 children used the new library. How many more adults than children used the library that week?

Use the library problem to review the subtraction strategy subtracting in parts. Have a volunteer explain how they would use this strategy.

Students might say:

"To subtract in parts, I can subtract 60 and then subtract 3. My equations are $85 - 60 = 25$ and $25 - 3 = 22$."

Increase the difficulty of the problem by changing the first sentence as follows: In the first month, 485 adults and 363 children used the new library. Now the numbers in the problem are larger. Can you still use the same strategy?

Ask students to solve $485 - 363$, using the same strategy.

Students might say:

"$485 - 100$ is 385, minus another 100 is 285, minus the last 100 is 185. So then I need to subtract $185 - 60$. It's kind of like the one we just did. $185 - 60 = 125$, then I just subtract 3 more."

Emphasize that the same strategies work for numbers of all sizes. The "chunks" that students use become larger, but the strategies stay the same.

Use the following problem as a second example. A small museum has 84 pictures and 37 statues. How many more pictures than statues do they have? After pairs have solved the problem, increase the difficulty by making the problem $584 - 237$.

ELL) **English Language Learners**

Rephrase Go over the activity again, rephrasing the main ideas. I can use the strategy *subtracting in parts* to find the difference between 85 and 63. I can use the same strategy *subtracting in parts* to find the difference between 485 and 363. These numbers are larger, but similar to 85 and 63.

Additional Resource

Student Math Handbook pages 13–15

Practice

30 MIN **INDIVIDUALS**

Choosing Starter Problems
Use anytime after Session 4.5.

Math Focus Points

◆ Solving subtraction problems by breaking numbers apart

Materials: R53

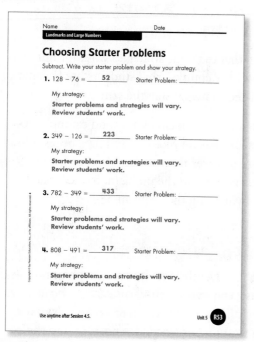

Use the class strategy charts to review the subtraction strategies students have been using. Show how to use your strategy for $458 - 273$. What starter problem will you use?

Have a volunteer explain their first step using his or her chosen strategy. Focus on subtracting in parts and adding up.

Students might say:

"My favorite strategy is breaking apart the second number to subtract in parts. I'd probably break 273 into $200 + 50 + 20 + 3$. I'd start with $458 - 200$."

If we started with $458 - 200$, what do we still have to solve? What would the next step be?

Have students complete the solution, subtracting the 50, 20, and 3 from 258.

Students might say:

"I like adding up. I would start with 273 and add 27 to get to 300."

If we started with $273 + 27 = 300$, what do we still have to solve? What would our next step be? Have students complete the solution. Encourage students to use a number line.

If we add 27 to get 300, 100 to get to 400, and then 58 to get to 458, what would that look like on a number line? What's our answer? As you and your students discuss the different subtraction strategies, record the strategy name and sample starter problem. Students' strategy names may differ from these examples.

$458 - 273$	
Strategy Name	Starter Problem
Subtracting in Parts	$458 - 200$
Adding Up	$273 + 27$
Adding Up	$273 + 100$

Distribute copies of Choosing Starter Problems (R53).

ELL **English Language Learners**

Suggest a Sequence Help students explain their strategies by providing this sequence of steps:

1. Choose a strategy.
2. Think about the steps you will use.
3. Write the starter problem.
4. Show the rest of the steps.

Additional Resource

Student Math Handbook pages 13–15

Extension

25 MIN | **INDIVIDUALS**

Change and Adjust

Use anytime after Session 4.4.

Math Focus Points

◆ Developing arguments about how the differences represented by two subtraction expressions are related (e.g., $432 - 198$ and $432 - 200$)

Materials: R54

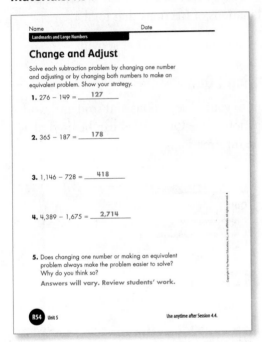

Here's a new question to think about. In addition, we changed both numbers and made an equivalent problem. What would that look like for subtraction? Solve $365 - 195$ by changing both numbers to make an equivalent problem. Use a representation or story context to prove the problems are equal.

Give students time to solve the problem and then discuss student solutions.

Students might say:

"I made up a story. I have 365 stickers and [Venetta] has 195. How many more do I have? Someone gave us each 5 more stickers. How many more do I have? See—it's the same amount. So, $365 - 195 = 370 - 200$!"

Distribute copies of Change and Adjust (R54).

ELL **English Language Learners**

Provide Sentence Stems Students may need help explaining the steps in these subtraction strategies. Provide a sentence stem for students to use. For example: I took 3 away from the second number, so I need to _____ (*take 3 away from the first number*).

Briefly review the subtraction strategies students have been using: subtracting in parts, adding up, and subtracting back. Today we're going to continue thinking about changing one number and then adjusting the difference. Start with $142 - 78$. Ask students to solve by starting with $142 - 80$, and to use a representation in their solution.

After students have solved the problem, have a brief discussion about their answers and representations.

Additional Resource

Student Math Handbook page 15

Differentiation in Investigation 1

Mathematics in This Investigation

The mathematics focuses on identifying fractional parts of the area of different rectangles or of groups of objects or people. The work also focuses on finding combinations of fractions that total 1.

Additional Resource: *Why Are Fractions Difficult? Developing Meaning for Fractions*, pages 139–140 (See Curriculum Unit 6)

Understanding the Mathematics

Students correctly identify the different fractional parts in 4×6 and 5×12 rectangles. They use related fractional parts (e.g., halves) to determine other fractional parts (e.g., fourths and eighths). They determine fractional parts of a group of objects or people and compare the parts accurately using different representations. Students add fractions with the same and related denominators. They use representations to add fractions and determine if the result is more than or less than 1.

Option: Assign the Extension activity.

Partially Understanding the Mathematics

Students identify many of the fractional parts in 4×6 rectangles correctly. They are able to determine some of the easier fractional parts (e.g., $\frac{1}{2}$ and $\frac{1}{4}$), but they have difficulty with other fractions. Students are most comfortable determining fractional parts in the context of the area of a rectangle, and they may struggle with looking at fractional parts of a group of objects or people. They can add fractions with the same denominator and use representations to find combinations of fractions that total 1.

Option: Assign the Practice activity.

Not Understanding the Mathematics

Students do not understand fractional parts and are not able to identify different fractions. They may recognize the value of $\frac{1}{2}$ in the context of the area of a rectangle, but struggle with other fractions. They do not make the connection to fractional parts of a group of objects or people, and they see the two ideas as independent of each other. It is difficult for these students to use representations to add fractions and find combinations of fractions that total 1.

Option: Assign the Intervention activity.

Investigation 1 Quiz

In addition to your observations and students' work in Investigation 1, the Quiz (R55) can be used to gather more information.

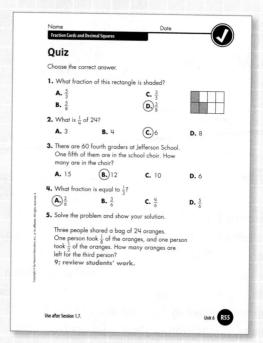

Intervention

20 MIN   PAIRS

Folding Fractions

Use anytime after Session 1.1.

Math Focus Points

◆ Finding fractional parts of a rectangular area

◆ Interpreting the meaning of the numerator and the denominator of a fraction

Vocabulary: fraction, numerator, denominator

Materials: blank paper, scissors (optional)

. . . .

Show two sheets of paper, one folded in half and the other folded into 2 parts that are not halves. Hold up the sheet folded in half. Is this sheet of paper folded in half? How do you know?

Students might say:

"The sheet of paper is folded in half. I can tell because when you fold it, the 2 pieces are the same size."

Have a volunteer write the fraction for $\frac{1}{2}$ on the board. Label the numerator and denominator.

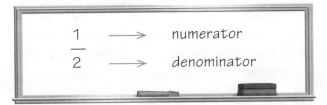

$$\frac{1}{2} \longrightarrow \begin{array}{l} \text{numerator} \\ \text{denominator} \end{array}$$

What does the denominator of the fraction show? What does the numerator show?

Be sure students understand that the 2 halves must be the same size. Hold up the sheet of paper that is folded into 2 parts that are not halves. Point to one of the parts. This paper is folded into 2 parts. This is one of the 2 parts. Why doesn't the fraction $\frac{1}{2}$ describe this part?

Fold sheets of paper so some show fourths and others do not. Here are some examples.

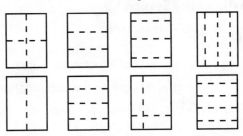

Give one of these rectangles to each pair. Is your sheet of paper folded into fourths? How do you know? If desired, allow students to cut the sheet of paper along the dashed lines so they can see if the pieces are the same size.

Have pairs take turns telling why their rectangle is or is not folded into fourths and demonstrating why they think so. For sheets that are divided into fourths, have students write the fraction $\frac{1}{4}$ on each section. How can you tell if a rectangle is folded into fourths?

Students might say:

"It has to be folded into 4 pieces and all of the pieces have to be the same size."

ELL **English Language Learners**

Provide a Word List To help students remember the terms *numerator* and *denominator* and their meanings, use a drawing like the one shown on this page and add the meanings of the terms: *denominator,* the total number of equal pieces; *numerator,* the number of pieces you are talking about.

Additional Resource

Student Math Handbook pages 53–57

Practice

20 MIN   PAIRS

Fractional Parts of a Rectangle
Use anytime after Session 1.5.

Math Focus Points
◆ Finding fractional parts of a rectangular area
◆ Writing, reading, and applying fraction notation

Materials: blank paper (4 sheets per pair), rulers, R56

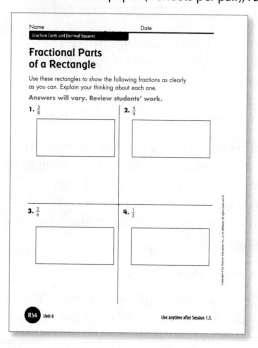

Distribute 4 pieces of blank paper to each pair. Ask students to shade $\frac{3}{4}$ of one sheet.

Most students will fold the paper or just estimate $\frac{3}{4}$, but allow students to use rulers or other measuring tools if they want. When they are finished, have them share their techniques.

Students might say:

"We folded the paper in half and then folded it in half again. That made 4 parts. Then we colored 3 parts."

Write the following fractions on the board.

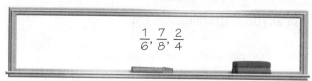

$$\frac{1}{6}, \frac{7}{8}, \frac{2}{4}$$

Use the sheets of paper to shade rectangles that show these fractions.

Discuss the different strategies each pair used to complete their fraction work. Did you use the same technique for each fraction?

Students might say:

"$\frac{1}{6}$ was the hardest because we couldn't start by folding the paper in half."

Have students exchange and compare methods for finding the fractional parts of the rectangles.

Distribute copies of Fractional Parts of a Rectangle (R56).

ELL English Language Learners

Partner Talk Review the meaning of the following words and encourage students to use them in their explanations: *fraction, numerator,* and *denominator.* Pair ELLs of different language proficiency to give them practice with English. Have the more proficient speaker choose one of the fractions and explain how the shading represents the fraction. Then have the other student repeat using a different fraction.

Additional Resource
Student Math Handbook pages 54, 56–57

Extension

20 MIN PAIRS

How Many?

Use anytime after Session 1.4.

Math Focus Points

◆ Finding fractional parts of a rectangular area

◆ Finding fractional parts of a group (of objects, people, etc.)

Materials: M11 (1 per pair), R57

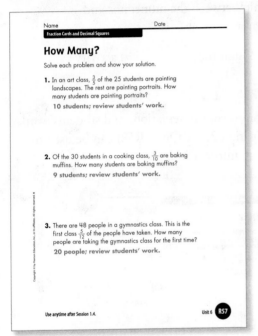

. . . .

Remind students that they found fractional parts on the 5 × 12 rectangle. What strategies did you use to find the number of squares in $\frac{1}{5}$ of the rectangle?

Students might say:

"One side of the rectangle is 5 units, so each row would be $\frac{1}{5}$. Each fifth is 12 square units."

Have students share strategies. How can knowing the number of squares in $\frac{1}{5}$ of the area help you find the number of squares in $\frac{1}{10}$ of the area?

Students might say:

"One tenth is half of $\frac{1}{5}$. One fifth is 12 square units, so $\frac{1}{10}$ is half of that, or 6 square units. So, I would shade 6 squares to show $\frac{1}{10}$."

Give each pair a copy of 5 × 12 Rectangles (M11). Have pairs work together to shade $\frac{3}{20}$ of the rectangle. How can you find the number of squares in $\frac{1}{20}$ of the rectangle? How can you use that to shade $\frac{3}{20}$ of the rectangle?

When students are finished, have them compare their answers and share their methods. Then write these fractions on the board and have pairs work together to shade rectangles for each fraction.

$$\frac{4}{15}, \frac{6}{30}$$

As they work, ask questions such as these:

◆ How many squares are in $\frac{1}{15}$ of a rectangle? How many squares are in $\frac{4}{15}$?

◆ How many squares are in $\frac{1}{30}$ of a rectangle? Did you use the number of squares in $\frac{1}{15}$ to find the number in $\frac{1}{30}$?

Distribute copies of How Many? (R57).

ELL English Language Learners

Use Repetition Some English Language Learners may have difficulty naming fractions with larger denominators. For example, students might say *fifteen* rather than *fifteenth* or *thirty* rather than *thirtieth*. As you write fractions, orally model how the fraction is read. As students write fractions, have them practice saying them orally.

Additional Resource

Student Math Handbook pages 56–57

Differentiation in Investigation 2

Mathematics in This Investigation

The mathematics focuses on making representations for fractions and ordering and comparing fractions using landmarks $0, \frac{1}{2}, 1$, and 2.

Additional Resource: *Strategies for Comparing Fractions*, pages 151–152 (See Curriculum Unit 6)

Understanding the Mathematics

Students understand what fractions are and understand the relationship between the numerator and denominator. They use landmarks and representations of fractions to determine their size, compare them, and place them accurately on a number line from least to greatest. They recognize equivalent fractions and place them on the number line. Students use related fractions and reasoning to determine the placement of more challenging fractions.

Option: Assign the Extension activity.

Partially Understanding the Mathematics

Students correctly compare fractions using landmarks, but may have some errors in their ordering. They are able to determine fraction equivalence with fractions equal to landmarks $(0, \frac{1}{2}, 1, 2)$, but struggle with other equivalents. They can locate obvious equivalent fractions (e.g., $\frac{1}{2}$ and $\frac{2}{4}$), but may not be able to recognize all equivalent fractions in a given list. They sometimes confuse the values of the numerator and denominator.

Option: Assign the Practice activity.

Not Understanding the Mathematics

Students do not understand what fractions are or how to order fractions correctly. They are unable to make accurate representations of the fractions using fraction cards or any other context. Students have difficulty finding equivalent fractions. When placing fractions from least to greatest on a number line, they may look for the largest digit to help determine the size of the fraction, not taking into account the relationship between the numerator and denominator.

Option: Assign the Intervention activity.

Investigation 2 Quiz

In addition to your observations and students' work in Investigation 2, the Quiz (R58) can be used to gather more information.

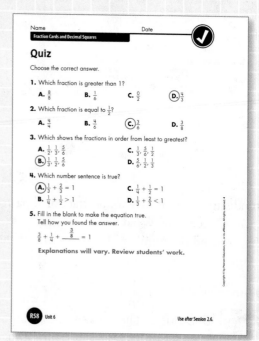

30 MIN **PAIRS**

Intervention

Comparing Fractions in Context

Use anytime after Session 2.3.

Math Focus Points

◆ Interpreting the meaning of the numerator and the denominator of a fraction

◆ Identifying equivalent fractions

◆ Ordering fractions and justifying their order through reasoning about fraction equivalencies and relationships

Materials: connecting cubes (24 per pair)

Read the following problem to students and write the facts on the board as shown.

Suppose I have 12 flowers. $\frac{7}{12}$ of the flowers are red. $\frac{2}{6}$ of the flowers are yellow. Are there more red or yellow flowers? How can you figure it out?

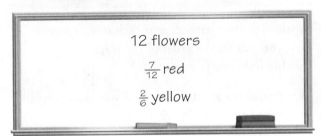

12 flowers

$\frac{7}{12}$ red

$\frac{2}{6}$ yellow

Have a volunteer illustrate the problem by using connecting cubes. What is $\frac{7}{12}$ of 12? Is $\frac{7}{12}$ more or less than $\frac{1}{2}$? Is $\frac{2}{6}$ more or less than $\frac{1}{2}$? How can you tell by looking at the fractions? Which fraction is larger?

Present the following problems to students and have them work together in pairs to solve them. Allow them to use drawings or connecting cubes to visualize the problem but emphasize reasoning techniques such as using $\frac{1}{2}$ as a landmark and finding equivalent fractions.

Imagine that you have a box of 8 muffins. You give a friend $\frac{5}{8}$ of the muffins. Who has more muffins—you or your friend?

In a case of 24 juice boxes, $\frac{2}{4}$ of the boxes are grape juice and $\frac{2}{8}$ of the boxes are orange juice. Are there more boxes of grape juice or boxes of orange juice?

There are 24 pieces of fruit in a bowl. $\frac{2}{6}$ are oranges, and $\frac{1}{3}$ are apples. Are there more apples or oranges?

Discuss the strategies students used to solve each problem by asking questions such as these:

◆ What fractions did you compare for the first problem?

◆ How did you compare the fractions $\frac{2}{4}$ and $\frac{2}{8}$?

Students might say:

 "$\frac{2}{4}$ is a half and $\frac{2}{8}$ is less than a half, so $\frac{2}{4}$ is more than $\frac{2}{8}$. There are more boxes of grape juice."

◆ How did you compare $\frac{2}{6}$ and $\frac{1}{3}$?

Students might say:

 "I used cubes. $\frac{2}{6}$ of 24 is 8, so there's 8 oranges. $\frac{1}{3}$ of 24 is 8. Oh—it's the same!"

> **ELL** English Language Learners
>
> **Rephrase** Some English Language Learners may need additional practice interpreting the numerators and denominators. Ask questions to focus on these meanings. For example: There are 8 muffins. Your friend gets $\frac{5}{8}$ of the muffins. How many muffins did your friend get? How many muffins do you have left? Is 5 *less than* 3? Is 5 *more than* 3? Who has more muffins?

Additional Resource

Student Math Handbook pages 54–55

Practice

20 MIN **PAIRS**

Fix the Order

Use anytime after Session 2.6.

Math Focus Points

◆ Ordering fractions and justifying their order through reasoning about fraction equivalencies and relationships

◆ Representing fractions using a number line

◆ Comparing fractions to the landmarks 0, $\frac{1}{2}$, 1, and 2

Materials: R59

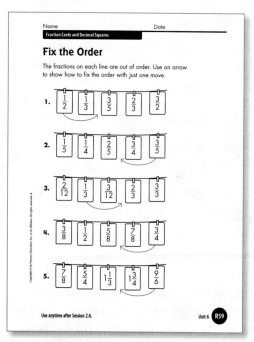

Write the following fractions on the board.

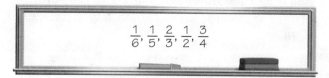

These fractions are not in order. How can you put them in order from least to greatest by moving only one fraction?

Assist students by asking questions such as:

◆ Is $\frac{1}{6}$ less than $\frac{1}{5}$? How do you know?

◆ Is $\frac{2}{3}$ less than $\frac{1}{2}$? How do you know?

◆ Is $\frac{2}{3}$ less than $\frac{3}{4}$? How do you know?

Have a volunteer draw an arrow from the fraction he or she wants to move to its new place. Students will probably observe that either $\frac{2}{3}$ can be moved right or $\frac{1}{2}$ can be moved left to reorder the numbers in one move.

Write these examples on the board.

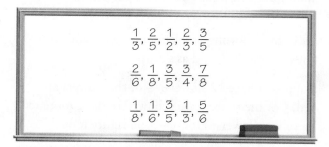

Work with your partner. For each row, figure out how you can fix the order of the fractions by moving only one fraction.

When students are finished, have volunteers explain how they compared the fractions.

Distribute copies of Fix the Order (R59).

ELL **English Language Learners**

Partner Talk English Language Learners may need additional practice using comparative terms such as *greater than* and *less than*. Pair ELLs of different language proficiency. Have partners take turns comparing two fractions at a time until they find the fraction that must be moved.

Additional Resource

Student Math Handbook
Game: *Capture Fractions* SMH G1
Materials: Fraction Cards

Extension

20 MIN   PAIRS

Challenging Fractions

Use anytime after Session 2.5.

Math Focus Points

◆ Ordering fractions and justifying their order through reasoning about fraction equivalencies and relationships

◆ Representing fractions using a number line

◆ Comparing fractions to the landmarks 0, $\frac{1}{2}$, 1, and 2

Materials: class fraction number line, self-stick notes, R60

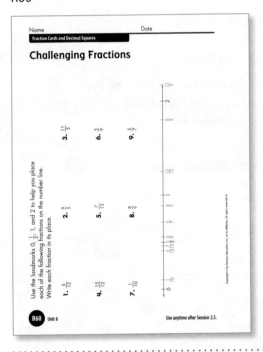

Write the following fractions on self-stick notes.

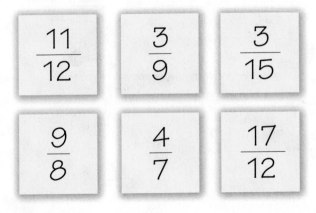

We are going to look at some fractions that we didn't make fraction cards for. Display the fraction card $\frac{4}{7}$. Where does this fraction go on the number line?

Students might say:

"Well, it's bigger than $\frac{1}{2}$, because half of 7 is $3\frac{1}{2}$. But it's just a little bigger so it's between $\frac{1}{2}$ and $\frac{5}{8}$."

Give each pair one of the self-stick notes and have pairs take turns placing their fractions on the number line. When everyone is finished, have each pair point out their fraction and explain how they selected the location for their self-stick note on the number line.

If two fractions have the same numerator and different denominators, how can you tell which one is greater? If two fractions have the same denominator and different numerators, how can you tell which one is greater?

If there is any disagreement about where a self-stick note should be placed on the number line, have students discuss the problem and come to an agreement on placement. Check to make sure the placement of fractions is correct.

Distribute copies of Challenging Fractions (R60).

> **ELL** **English Language Learners**
>
> **Model Thinking Aloud** Model your thinking for placing the fraction $\frac{9}{8}$ on the number line. Point to the landmark numbers on a number line to provide English Language Learners with a visual. I know that $\frac{9}{8}$ is more than 1. $\frac{9}{8}$ is close to $\frac{8}{8}$ which is equivalent to 1. So, I will place $\frac{9}{8}$ between 1 and $1\frac{1}{2}$, but closer to 1.

Additional Resource

Student Math Handbook pages 60–61

Differentiation in Investigation 3

Mathematics in This Investigation

The mathematics focuses on comparing decimals (tenths and hundredths) using representations and reasoning. There is also a focus on using representations to combine decimals.

Understanding the Mathematics

Students correctly read and create accurate representations for decimals using 10×10 squares. They accurately compare decimals by reasoning about the meaning of the numbers. When combining decimals, these students display the total using a representation, and they explain the value of the sum. Students also know whether their answer is reasonable as it relates to the numbers in the problem.

Option: Assign the Extension activity.

Partially Understanding the Mathematics

Students may read decimals correctly, but their representations using 10×10 squares may not always accurately reflect the decimals. They generally make correct comparisons between two different decimals, but initially they rely on the representation. Students are comfortable creating representations of one decimal, but they may encounter some difficulty when combining decimals and explaining the value of the sum. Students are developing some number sense in terms of decimal numbers, but still rely on representations to be certain of their answers.

Option: Assign the Practice activity.

Not Understanding the Mathematics

Students' representations do not demonstrate an understanding of decimals. Their comparisons do not correctly display which decimal is larger. They have difficulty determining the size of the decimals written in tenths and hundredths, and they get tenths and hundredths confused. These students only feel comfortable working with whole numbers. They do not combine decimals correctly, and they are not able to add decimals when one decimal is written in tenths and the other is written in hundredths. Students do not know what a reasonable answer is when adding decimals.

Option: Assign the Intervention activity.

Investigation 3 Quiz

In addition to your observations and students' work in Investigation 3, the Quiz (R61) can be used to gather more information.

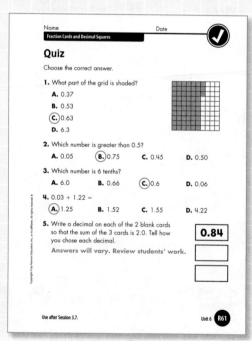

Intervention

25 MIN   PAIRS

Comparing to 0, $\frac{1}{2}$, and 1

Use anytime after Session 3.2.

Math Focus Points

◆ Reading and writing tenths and hundredths

◆ Representing tenths and hundreds as part of an area

◆ Ordering decimals and justifying their order through reasoning about representations and meaning of the numbers

Materials: blank paper, Decimal Cards (1 deck per pair), T67 (as needed), M15 (as needed)

· ·

Materials to Prepare: Draw a number line on the board as shown below.

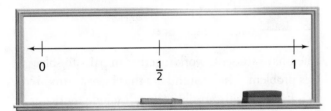

Ask students to copy the number line on a blank sheet of paper. Remind students that they located fractions on the number line in Session 2.5.

What decimal is the same as $\frac{1}{2}$? If students need help, display 10 × 10 Squares (T67) on the overhead and have a volunteer shade the squares to show $\frac{1}{2}$. Identify the fractions $\frac{5}{10}$ and $\frac{50}{100}$ as the decimals 0.5 and 0.50. Write 0.5 and 0.50 below $\frac{1}{2}$ on the number line.

Display the Decimal Card for seven tenths. Students should recognize that $\frac{7}{10}$ is the same as 0.7. Have a volunteer show $\frac{7}{10}$ on the 10 × 10 Squares. Figure out where your decimal goes on the number line. Is it between 0 and $\frac{1}{2}$ or between $\frac{1}{2}$ and 1? Is it closer to 0, $\frac{1}{2}$, or 1?

Students might say:

"Seven tenths is more than $\frac{1}{2}$. It is a little closer to $\frac{1}{2}$ than to 1."

Demonstrate where to label 0.7 on the number line on the board and have students do the same.

Distribute a deck of Decimal Cards to each pair of students. Have copies of 10 × 10 Squares (M15) available for students to color hundreds squares for their decimals.

Direct students to take turns naming their decimal, showing their drawings if they made them, and writing their number where they think it goes on the number line. Remind students to use the fractions 0, $\frac{1}{2}$, and 1 as a guide to place each decimal.

You may want to suggest to those students who need additional support to divide their number line into tenths. Have them start with the Decimal Cards for tenths and identify those decimals on the number line first. Then they can continue with the decimals for hundredths.

(**ELL**) **English Language Learners**

Model Thinking Aloud Using the number line on the board, model how to locate 0.85. I know that eighty-five hundredths is between $\frac{1}{2}$ and 1. It is more than eight tenths and less than nine tenths. So, I will put 0.85 halfway between 0.8 and 0.9.

Additional Resource

Student Math Handbook page 65

Practice

25 MIN   PAIRS

Adding Decimal Numbers

Use anytime after Session 3.5.

Math Focus Points

◆ Reading and writing tenths and hundredths

◆ Adding decimal numbers that are multiples of 0.1 and 0.25 (e.g., 2.3 and 3.25)

Materials: M15 (as needed), R62

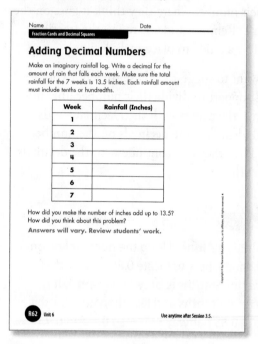

What number can you add to 2.75 to get a sum of 5.0? How can you figure it out?

Students might say:

"If you add 0.25 to 2.75, you get 3. Then you add 2 more to get 5.
2 + 0.25 = 2.25.
So, 2.75 + 2.25 = 5.0."

Write the following problem on the board.

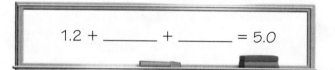

$$1.2 + \underline{\qquad} + \underline{\qquad} = 5.0$$

What two numbers can you add to 1.2 to get a sum of 5.0? How will you find them? Is there more than one way to complete the equation?

Have various students show different combinations and have the rest of the group check to see that the sum is 5. Check for understanding by asking the following questions:

◆ How did you choose the first number?

◆ How did you choose the second number?

Encourage students to use landmark decimals and combinations they know and to break decimals apart so that they can be easily added.

Students might say:

"I counted on from 1.2 to 2. That is 0.8, so 0.8 is my first number. Then I added 3 more to get to 5, so my second number is 3."

Then have students work together in pairs to solve this problem. Find 5 numbers that have a sum of 8.5. Each of your numbers must include tenths or hundredths. Allow students to use 10 × 10 Squares (M15) if they wish.

Distribute copies of Adding Decimal Numbers (R62).

ELL ▸ **English Language Learners**

Provide a Word List Write the words *sum, equation, tenths,* and *hundredths* on the board. Review the meaning of each with students. Some English Language Learners may confuse *sum* with *some, tenths* with *tens,* and *hundredths* with *hundreds.* Have students write or draw examples for each word to help them remember their meanings.

Additional Resource

Student Math Handbook

Game: *Fill Two* SMH G7

Materials: Decimal Cards, crayons or markers, M15

Extension

20 MIN **PAIRS**

Comparing Tenths and Hundredths

Use anytime after Session 3.2.

Math Focus Points

◆ Reading and writing tenths and hundredths

◆ Ordering decimals and justifying their order through reasoning about representations and meaning of the numbers

Materials: M15 (as needed), R63

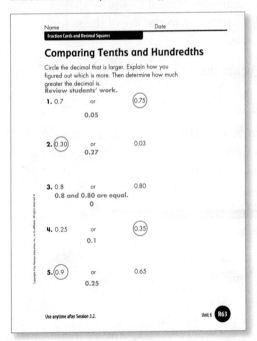

Write the following decimals on the board.

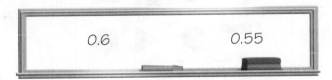

0.6   0.55

Which of these decimals is greater? How do you know?

Students might say:

"Fifty-five hundredths is halfway between 5 tenths and 6 tenths, so 0.6 is greater than 0.55."

How much greater is 0.6 than 0.55? How can you figure it out?

Students might say:

"I thought of 6 tenths as 60 hundredths. Then I subtracted 55 hundredths from 60 hundredths, just like I subtract whole numbers. So 0.60 − 0.55 = 0.05."

Present three more sets of decimals and have students work in pairs to decide which decimal in each pair is greater and how much greater it is. Allow students to use 10 × 10 Squares (M15) if needed.

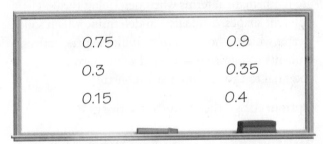

0.75	0.9
0.3	0.35
0.15	0.4

When students have finished, have them share their strategies for determining which decimal is greater and for calculating how much greater.

Distribute copies of Comparing Tenths and Hundredths (R63).

ELL **English Language Learners**

Use Repetition Some English Language Learners may struggle with comparative terms such as *greater*. Have students represent each pair of decimals using M15. Then ask them questions such as the following. How many squares did you color for [0.75]? How many squares did you color for [0.9]? How many *more* squares did you color for [0.9] than [0.75]? So, how much greater is [0.9] than [0.75]?

Additional Resource

Student Math Handbook page 69

Differentiation in Investigation 1

Mathematics in This Investigation

The mathematics focuses on describing properties and attributes of geometric solids. The work also focuses on identifying the silhouettes of these solids from different perspectives.

Additional Resource: *Difficulties in Visualizing Silhouettes*, pages 97–98 (See Curriculum Unit 7)

Understanding the Mathematics

Students describe the solids using both the properties and attributes particular to each solid. They recognize the geometric solids by name and use mathematical terms when describing the different shapes. Students can determine which solid creates which silhouettes from multiple perspectives. Students recognize that curved solids have the potential to cast rectangular silhouettes.

Option: Assign the **Extension** activity.

Partially Understanding the Mathematics

Students describe the geometric solids using properties and attributes, but they may connect the different shapes and their attributes incorrectly. Students don't identify all the attributes of solids. They recognize some, but not all, of the shapes by name. When looking at the different silhouettes of the shapes, these students may not recognize the shapes from multiple perspectives.

Option: Assign the **Practice** activity.

Not Understanding the Mathematics

Students are not able to accurately describe the different properties and attributes of geometric solids. They cannot recognize the different shapes by name and have difficulty determining the differences between similar shapes. When comparing the shapes, they may use general terms (e.g., *ball, box*) instead of the correct mathematical terms. They are not able to determine the shapes correctly from their silhouettes. Students may only connect the idea that round silhouettes are created by round shapes and square silhouettes are created by square shapes, and pay little attention to the size of the shape and silhouette.

Option: Assign the **Intervention** activity.

Investigation 1 Quiz

In addition to your observations and students' work in Investigation 1, the Quiz (R64) can be used to gather more information.

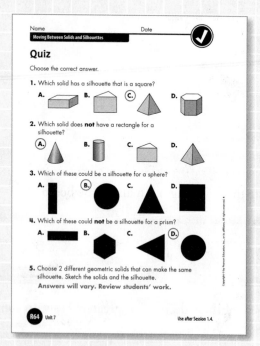

Intervention

25 MIN   INDIVIDUALS

City Street

Use anytime after Session 1.3.

Math Focus Points

◆ Understanding how 3-D solids project silhouettes with 2-D shapes (for example, how a cone can produce both triangular and circular silhouettes)

Vocabulary: cube, cylinder, square pyramid, square prism, triangular prism, silhouette

Materials: geometric solids, toy figures, *Student Activity Book* p. 1, R65

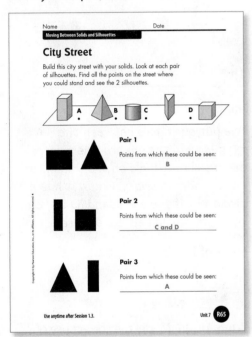

Have students find these 5 solids.

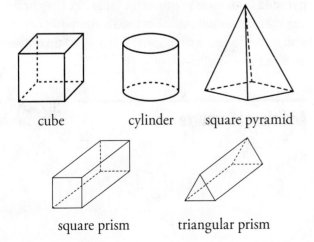

cube   cylinder   square pyramid

square prism   triangular prism

Use page 1 of the *Student Activity Book* to review the names of the 5 solids. Have students place each solid on the drawing with its name.

Now, let's put these solids in a row to make buildings on a city street. Distribute copies of City Street (R65). Arrange your buildings to make this street. The square prism comes first. What comes next? Have students name the solids from left to right. Check that the prisms are standing on their bases as shown.

Have students focus on the first two buildings and the spot marked A. Imagine you are standing at point A. If you turn one way, you see a rectangle. What do you see if you turn the other way? Have students use a toy figure to help them imagine standing at point A.

To verify that students will see a rectangle and a triangle from point A, have 3 students stand in a row. Hand the square prism to the left student and the pyramid to the right student. Have the students hold the solids at eye level. Ask the student in the middle: What silhouette do you see if you turn right? What if you turn left?

Talk about what silhouettes students would see from points B, C, and D. Then have pairs work together to finish page R65.

ELL English Language Learners

Rephrase Some English Language Learners may have difficulty with the word *silhouette*. Rephrase questions to use terms with which they are more familiar, such as *outline* or *shadow*.

Additional Resource

Student Math Handbook pages 122–123

Practice

20 MIN | GROUPS

Landscape 4

Use anytime after Session 1.4.

Math Focus Points

◆ Visualizing what 3-D figures look like from different perspectives

Vocabulary: silhouette

Materials: *Student Activity Book* p. 1, geometric solids, toy figures (1 per group), R66

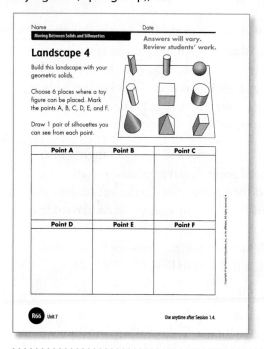

see the solids from the figure's viewpoint. The example below illustrates what students may do in the activity.

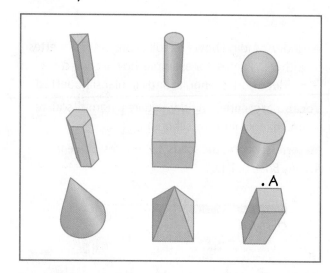

Students might say:

 "We put our figure between the cylinder and the square prism. I would see a tall rectangle on the prism, but the cylinder is tricky. I know it has a circle, but if you are standing at Point A, all you would see is a square."

Distribute copies of Landscape 4 (R66).

Use page 1 of the *Student Activity Book* to review the names of the geometric solids. Then have students take turns choosing a solid from the set and telling what silhouette(s) that solid makes. Which solid makes 1 silhouette only? Which solids make a tall rectangle? What about a square? What about a circle?

Work in your group and choose 9 solids to make a landscape. Arrange the solids in 3 rows and 3 columns. Put at least 3 inches between each pair of solids so there is room to place a toy figure.

Put your toy figure any place in the landscape. Label that place point A. What silhouettes can you see from that point? Students can crouch down to

---

ELL **English Language Learners**

Model Thinking Aloud Model the correct use of geometric language by contrasting pairs of solids. For example: The triangular prism and the square pyramid both have triangles for faces. So, they both can make triangular silhouettes. The pyramid could also make a square silhouette, but only if I tip it over on one side.

Additional Resource

Student Math Handbook pages 122–123

Extension

30 MIN **GROUPS**

Three-Landscape Challenge

Use anytime after Session 1.4.

Math Focus Points

◆ Understanding how 3-D solids project silhouettes with 2-D shapes (for example, how a cone can produce both triangular and circular silhouettes)

◆ Visualizing what 3-D figures look like from different perspectives

Vocabulary: silhouette

Materials: geometric solids; *Student Activity Book* pp. 1, 7, 11, and 12

On the board, list the names of all the geometric solids from page 1 of the *Student Activity Book*. Refer to the first cylinder as the *long cylinder*, and the second cylinder as the *short cylinder*. Discuss with students the possible silhouettes these geometric solids can make. Record student responses and discuss their observations.

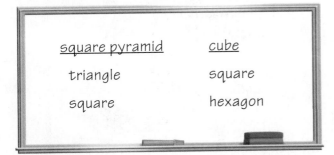

square pyramid   cube

triangle   square

square   hexagon

Students might say:

"The sphere is the only solid with just 1 silhouette. I can get more than 1 silhouette for a cube if I turn it at different angles. I can see a hexagon if I look right at one corner of the cube."

When the same silhouette occurs in different sizes, have students describe each silhouette as, for example, a *small circle* and a *large circle*.

Have students stand the solids up as if they were buildings in a landscape. What silhouettes can no longer be seen? Students should notice, for example, that the cone has only a triangular silhouette when it is standing on its base.

Have students work in groups and refer to landscapes 1, 2, and 3 on *Student Activity Book* pages 7, 11, and 12. Decide together whether to interpret each "round solid" as a sphere or a hemisphere.

Have students begin by finding the points in all 3 landscapes from which they can see a circle and a square. Repeat for a triangle and a rectangle that is not a square. Then present the group activity. One member in your group should choose any 2 of the silhouettes from the class list we have made. Your challenge is to find *all* the points in the 3 landscapes from which the 2 silhouettes can be seen.

Encourage groups to solve the problems by looking at the landscape diagrams only, rather than building the landscapes. Group members take turns choosing the pair of silhouettes. Students should record each pair of silhouettes chosen as well as the corresponding points.

> **ELL**) **English Language Learners**
>
> **Partner Talk** Have pairs discuss prisms. Motivate the discussion with questions, such as the following: What does the name of the prism tell you about its silhouettes? What shape is a silhouette for *any* prism? Encourage students to use the geometric solids to point to and describe the shapes they see.

Additional Resource

Student Math Handbook pages 122–123

Differentiation in Investigation 2

Mathematics in This Investigation

The mathematics focuses on translating between 2- and 3-dimensional shapes by drawing silhouettes of 3-dimensional cube buildings from different perspectives.

Additional Resource: *Accommodations in an Inclusion Classroom: Silhouettes of Cube Buildings,* pages 77–79 (See *Implementing Investigations in Grade 4*)

Understanding the Mathematics

Students easily construct cube buildings using connecting cubes. They accurately translate between 2-D pictures and the 3-D cube buildings they create. Students draw all of the cubes in a given silhouette, including the recessed cubes, and they can properly orient the cube building to reflect the perspective from which they are looking. They also draw the silhouettes without making the cube buildings.

Option: Assign the Extension activity.

Partially Understanding the Mathematics

Students construct cube buildings using connecting cubes, but they may not discern all of the cubes from the 2-D images, leaving their buildings incomplete. They translate between the 2-D images and 3-D buildings, but they may struggle with shapes having more cubes and with looking from different perspectives. When drawing from a silhouette, they may not recognize all the recessed cubes, so they do not include them in their representations. They are comfortable drawing the silhouettes from one perspective, usually the front, but they are not as fluent from other perspectives.

Option: Assign the Practice activity.

Not Understanding the Mathematics

Students have difficulty building the 3-D cube buildings from the 2-D images. They are not able to translate between the cubes on the paper and the cubes in the buildings they are asked to construct. When drawing the silhouettes for a given building, they miss many of the cubes, resulting in an incorrect silhouette. Students struggle with the different perspectives. They may confuse which perspective is which and how it relates to both the cube building and its silhouette.

Option: Assign the Intervention activity.

Investigation 2 Quiz

In addition to your observations and students' work in Investigation 2, the Quiz (R67) can be used to gather more information.

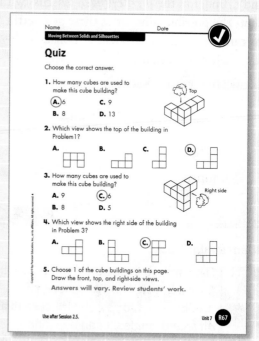

Intervention

25 MIN **PAIRS**

Sizes of Cube Buildings

Use anytime after Session 2.1.

Math Focus Points

◆ Recognizing how components of 3-D cube buildings come together to form the whole building

Vocabulary: volume

Materials: connecting cubes (about 80 per pair)

....

Materials to Prepare: Make the cube buildings shown in the activity. ($1 \times 2 \times 3$, $2 \times 2 \times 3$, $2 \times 2 \times 4$, $2 \times 4 \times 3$)

Show students the first pair ($1 \times 2 \times 3$, $2 \times 2 \times 3$) of buildings and have pairs of students make and examine them.

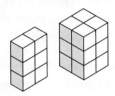

How can we compare the sizes of these cube buildings? Point out that the height of a building isn't a very good way to measure its size. A building's height changes depending on how it is positioned (e.g., some buildings can be turned so that they are tall or flat).

One way to measure building size is to count the number of cubes in the building. This is the *volume*. Volume is a measure of how much space is in the cube building. How many cubes are in each of these buildings?

Have pairs find the volume of the two cube buildings. Some students will want to take the buildings completely apart and count the cubes individually. Others may not need to do this. Help students see that one building is made of 6 cubes and the other has 12.

Show students the second pair ($2 \times 2 \times 4$, $2 \times 4 \times 3$) of buildings and have pairs of students make and examine them.

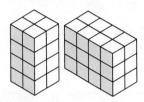

Ask pairs to find the volume of each building. This time, try to think of a way to count the cubes without counting each one.

Students might say:

"In the tall building, there are 4 layers. I counted 4 cubes in the top layer, so I counted by 4s. 4, 8, 12, 16."

ELL **English Language Learners**

Use Repetition Students sometimes confuse *area* and *volume* and related terminology. Ask questions, such as, Would you use squares or cubes to measure *volume*? Each time students count the cubes in a cube building, emphasize that they are finding the building's volume.

Additional Resource

Student Math Handbook page 124

Practice

25 MIN   GROUPS

More City Views

Use anytime after Session 2.5.

Math Focus Points

◆ Drawing silhouettes of 3-D cube buildings from different perspectives

Vocabulary: silhouette, view

Materials: connecting cubes, M7 (from Unit 3), R68

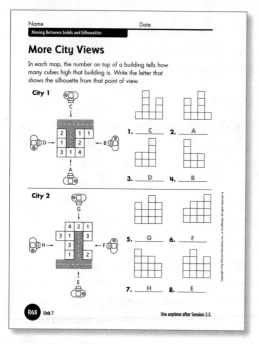

....

Draw the following cube city map on the board.

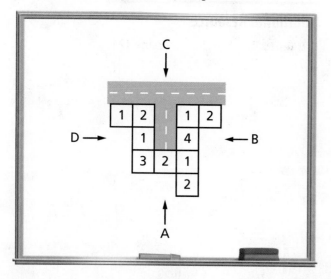

This map shows the top view of a cube city with 10 buildings. The number on each building tells how many cubes tall that building is. Give each student a copy of Centimeter Grid Paper (M7) and distribute connecting cubes to each group. On the grid paper, draw the silhouette you'd see from Point A. Label your silhouette A. You may use cubes to help. Have students work in their groups to solve the problem. Then discuss their results and explain their thinking.

Students might say:

"We figured we'd see the top of the tallest buildings, even if they're behind shorter buildings. We started at the left. Our silhouette is 1 square tall, then 3, then 2, then 4, and then 2."

Now draw the other three views: from point B, from point C, and from point D. Have students compare their drawings with other members of their group and attempt to resolve any discrepancies.

When all the views are sketched, have groups use connecting cubes to build the city on a sheet of paper with the labels A, B, C, and D written in the appropriate locations. The group should check their silhouettes against the cube city.

Distribute copies of More City Views (R68).

ELL   English Language Learners

Partner Talk Have pairs take turns choosing a view of the city map (A,B,C, or D), and describe how their sketch matches the cube city. Beginning English Language Learners may only be able to use short, simple phrases. Encourage more proficient speakers to use words such as *silhouette* or *view* in their explanations.

Additional Resource

Student Math Handbook page 124

Extension

Six Views of Cube Buildings
Use anytime after Session 2.3.

Math Focus Points
◆ Drawing silhouettes of 3-D cube buildings from different perspectives

Vocabulary: silhouette, view

Materials: connecting cubes, blank paper, T75, M7 (from Unit 3), R69

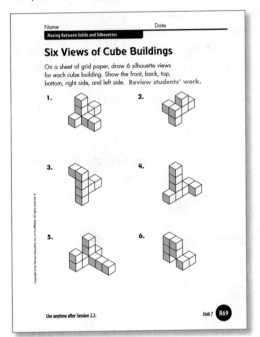

Display Image 8 of the transparency Quick Images: 3-D (T75).

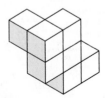

You've been drawing front, top, and right-side silhouettes of cube buildings. Today you are going to draw three more silhouettes, the back, the bottom, and the left side.

Have pairs work together to make sketches on Centimeter Grid Paper (M7) showing their visualization of the six views of the cube building. Remind them that the shaded side is the front, and there are no hidden cubes.

When students have finished their drawings, have them label *front, back, left,* and *right* along appropriate edges of a blank sheet of paper. Ask students to use connecting cubes to construct the cube building on the sheet of paper. Students should use their building to verify their drawings of the six views, making corrections as needed. The six views are shown below.

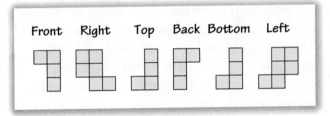

How are the front and back silhouettes related? Which other pairs of silhouettes have this same relationship?

Students will need additional sheets of Centimeter Grid Paper to complete Six Views of Cube Buildings (R69).

ELL English Language Learners

Model Thinking Aloud Use gestures to reinforce the meanings of the words *front, back, left, right, top,* and *bottom.* During discussion, periodically ask students to do the same to confirm that they are understanding the meaning of each word.

Additional Resource

Student Math Handbook page 124

Differentiation in Investigation 3

Mathematics in This Investigation

The mathematics focuses on finding the volume of rectangular prisms using cubic units.

Additional Resource: *Strategies for Finding the Number of Cubes in 3-D Arrays*, pages 103–105 (See Curriculum Unit 7)

Understanding the Mathematics

Students understand volume. They use the box patterns accurately to predict and then determine the volume of the prisms by considering how many cubes are in one layer and how many layers are in the prism. Students understand the relationship between the rectangular prism and the squares in the pattern, and they can figure out how many layers are needed. They are able to find the volume without building the prism. They understand how changing the dimensions of a box affects how many cubes will fit in the box.

Option: Assign the Extension activity.

Partially Understanding the Mathematics

Students are developing their understanding of volume. They can build the box from the pattern, but initially struggle to build the prism from connecting cubes. Once the prism is built, students need repeated practice to be certain all cubes are counted. They often build the box pattern around the rectangular prism to ensure they have the correct amount of cubes. In order to determine how many layers are needed, students often build the entire prism and check it against the box pattern. They do not completely understand how changing the dimensions of a box affects how many cubes will fit in the box.

Option: Assign the Practice activity.

Not Understanding the Mathematics

Students do not understand volume. They struggle to make the connection between building the rectangular prisms and how that relates to measuring the volume of a shape. When using the box patterns, they will try to build the rectangular prisms to determine volume, but they often make prisms with incorrect measurements. They are typically unable to make a box pattern for a box that holds a given number of cubes. They see the box patterns and rectangular prisms as separate ideas, not realizing that one connects to the other. They do not understand how changing the dimensions of a box affects how many cubes will fit in the box.

Option: Assign the Intervention activity.

Investigation 3 Quiz

In addition to your observations and students' work in Investigation 3, the Quiz (R70) can be used to gather more information.

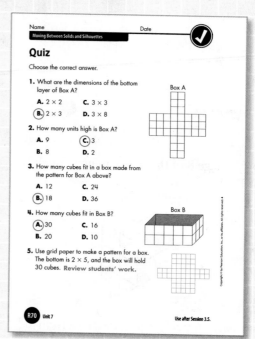

Intervention

Making Box Patterns

Use anytime after Session 3.2.

Math Focus Points

◆ Designing patterns for boxes that hold a given number of cubes (volume)

Vocabulary: rectangular prism, layer, rectangle

Materials: connecting cubes, colored pencils, scissors, tape, M21 (2 per student)

· ·

Have each student use connecting cubes to make a 2 × 4 × 2 rectangular prism. Set your prism down on a side that is 4 cubes long and 2 cubes wide.

Today you will make a pattern for a box that can hold this rectangular prism. Give each student a copy of Three-Quarter-Inch Grid Paper (M21). The pattern for the box will have a bottom and 4 sides. Start by outlining the bottom of the box on your grid paper. Help students position the rectangle vertically in the center of the grid paper. After students outline the 4 × 2 rectangle, have them color it in.

Put your prism on the colored rectangle on the grid paper. To make the sides of the box, you have to know how tall it needs to be. How many layers tall is the rectangular prism?

Point out how the sides need to extend out 2 squares away from the bottom. This will make the pattern 2 cubes tall—just like the prism made out of cubes. Have students color the 4 sides a different color from the bottom of the box. What shape is each side? Are all 4 sides the same? Help students match each side of the box pattern with a face of the prism.

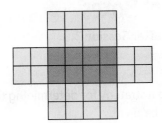

Cut out your pattern and fold into a box with the grid lines on the *outside* of the box. Tape the edges, but leave one side untaped to make it easier to slip the prism into the box. Check that the student's prism fits inside the assembled box.

What is the volume of this box? How does knowing how many cubes are in one layer, and how many layers there are, help us find the volume?

Take the prism out of the box and put another 2 × 4 layer on it. If you make a pattern for a box for this new prism, how will it be the same as the first pattern? How will it be different? Give each student another copy of Three-Quarter-Inch Grid Paper. Have students make a pattern for a box for the larger prism. When they've finished, have a discussion about the volume of the new box, using what they know about the layers.

> **ELL** **English Language Learners**
>
> **Rephrase** There are many steps students need to follow in this activity. As you discuss them, rephrase and use gestures to be sure students understand words such as *bottom, tall,* and *layer.*

Additional Resource

Student Math Handbook pages 125–126

Practice

25 MIN **GROUPS**

Volume of Boxes

Use anytime after Session 3.3.

Math Focus Points

◆ Developing a strategy for determining the volume of rectangular prisms

Vocabulary: rectangular prism, volume

Materials: connecting cubes, scissors, tape, M21 (about 5 per student), R71

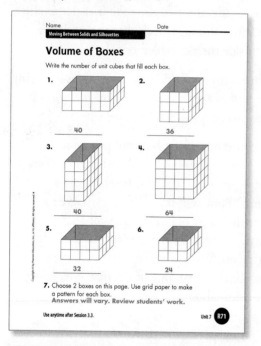

Name _____ Date _____
Moving Between Solids and Silhouettes

Volume of Boxes

Write the number of unit cubes that fill each box.

1. 40   2. 36

3. 40   4. 64

5. 32   6. 24

7. Choose 2 boxes on this page. Use grid paper to make a pattern for each box.
Answers will vary. Review students' work.

Use anytime after Session 3.3.   Unit 7 **R71**

. . . .

Materials to Prepare: Using connecting cubes, build a 3 × 4 × 5 prism for each group.

Distribute the prisms to the groups. How many cubes did I use to make the rectangular prism? Talk it over in your group. See if you can figure it out without taking the prism apart.

Students might say:

"We counted how many cubes were on top. We got 20. Then we multiplied by 3 because the prism is 3 layers high. We think you used 60 cubes."

Before you take the prism apart to see if you're right, draw a pattern for a box for this prism. Provide copies of Three-Quarter-Inch Grid Paper (M21). Tell students they will need to tape two or more grids together. Suggest that they cut off the extra paper around each grid before joining them. Use some of the completed patterns to point out how there is more than one way to draw a correct pattern. Then have students set the patterns aside.

Now you can take apart the prism and count the cubes. Did you have the right answer earlier? Remind students that when they determine the number of cubes in a prism, they are finding its volume.

Take a look at the box pattern you made. Suppose you had *only* the pattern. How could you figure out the number of cubes that would fit in the box without actually making the box? Does it matter if the bottom of your box is different from another student's?

Distribute copies of Volume of Boxes (R71). Students need additional copies of M21 to complete R71.

ELL English Language Learners

Provide a Word List Discuss the meanings of the words *volume, layers,* and *dimensions.* Then have students use those words to describe the 3 × 4 × 5 prism made out of cubes.

Additional Resource

Student Math Handbook pages 125–126

Extension

20 MIN **GROUPS**

Half or Twice as Many

Use anytime after Session 3.3.

Math Focus Points

◆ Doubling the number of cubes for a given box and considering how that changes the dimensions of the original box

Vocabulary: dimensions, volume, layer, factor

Materials: connecting cubes (as needed), scissors (as needed), tape, M21 (as needed), R72

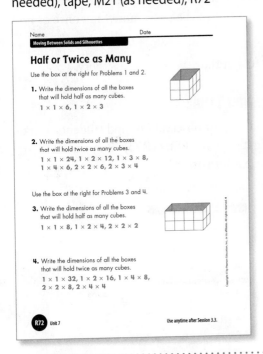

Begin by having students make a pattern for a box that will hold 24 cubes. Pick up two student-made patterns that have the same bottom dimensions but are oriented differently. Rotate one pattern to demonstrate that these drawings show the same box pattern from two different views. Then pick up two patterns that have different bottom dimensions. Have students verify that each box will hold 24 cubes even though the dimensions are different.

Ask students if all the possible dimensions for the box have been accounted for. If not, ask them which other dimensions are possible.

Suppose you need a box with half the volume. How many cubes would that be? Your challenge is to find the dimensions of *all* the possible boxes that have half the volume.

Have students work in their groups to solve the problem. They can use any strategies or materials, such as building boxes from connecting cubes, sketching patterns on Three-Quarter-Inch Grid Paper (M21), or making 2-D drawings of boxes.

Students might say:

"We started by making boxes with just 1 layer. We got 3 of those: $1 \times 1 \times 12$, $1 \times 2 \times 6$, and $1 \times 3 \times 4$. Then we did 2 layers, and the only new one was $2 \times 2 \times 3$. When we did more layers, we were just repeating the other boxes."

"You don't have to build any boxes. You can use the factors of 12 and get the dimensions of the 4 boxes."

Repeat the activity by having students find all the possible boxes with *double* the volume of the original box. *(There are 9 possibilities.)*

Distribute copies of Half or Twice as Many (R72).

ELL **English Language Learners**

Rephrase Use drawings and models to help students understand that the word *dimensions* refers to linear measures for describing 2-D and 3-D shapes. Hold up plane shapes and geometric solids as you point out dimensions such as length, width, and height.

Additional Resource

Student Math Handbook pages 125–126

Differentiation in Investigation 1

Mathematics in This Investigation

The mathematics focuses on solving multiplication problems with 2-digit numbers.

Additional Resource: *The Case of Maura: Now That I Know the Exact Answer I Can Figure Out the Estimate: Helping a Student Understand Estimation,* pages 81–83 (See *Implementing Investigations in Grade 4*)

Understanding the Mathematics

Students have a strong understanding of the operation of multiplication, and they solve problems accurately and efficiently using different strategies. They make estimates, use multiples of 10, and use cluster problems by choosing which expressions in the cluster will best help them to solve the given multiplication problem successfully. They also create a story context which displays an understanding of multiplication. Students use representations to explain and justify their solutions.

Option: Assign the Extension activity.

Partially Understanding the Mathematics

Students solve 2-digit multiplication problems, but they are less efficient in finding solutions. Instead of using multiples of 10 to solve 2-digit problems, they may multiply repeatedly only by 10. Students may use representations and story problems to help them solve the problem, rather than using them to explain their solutions. When breaking the numbers apart, students may have some difficulty keeping track of the different parts, possibly leading to incorrect solutions.

Option: Assign the Practice activity.

Not Understanding the Mathematics

Students do not understand how to multiply 2-digit numbers and are still only comfortable with single-digit multiplication. Their estimates do not make sense within the context of the numbers of the problem, and the representations they create do not help to lead to a solution. Students often make mistakes when multiplying by multiples of 10. They might be using repeated addition to solve problems. When breaking the numbers apart, they are not able to keep track of the different parts. They may end up multiplying some of the parts more than once or not at all.

Option: Assign the Intervention activity.

Investigation 1 Quiz

In addition to your observations and students' work in Investigation 1 the Quiz (R73) can be used to gather more information.

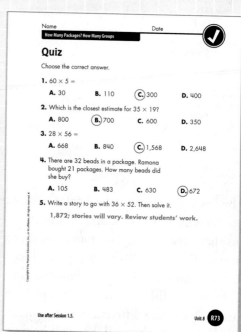

Intervention

30 MIN **PAIRS**

The 10th, 20th, and 30th Multiples

Use anytime after Session 1.2.

Math Focus Points

◆ Solving 2-digit multiplication problems by breaking a problem into smaller parts and combining the subproducts

Materials: 3 × 3 self-stick notes or 5-foot strips of paper about 2″ wide

. . . .

Write 23 × 41 = on the board. One way to solve this problem is to make a multiple tower for 41. How many multiples of 41 would we need?

Using either self-stick notes or long strips of paper, have pairs of students start the multiple tower. Ask them to pause when they get to the 10th multiple. Do you need to show every multiple of 41 to solve this problem? Which ones are the important ones?

Students might say:

"We know we need the 23rd multiple. We could do the 10th multiple, then the 20th multiple, and then do a few more to get to the 23rd."

That sounds like a good plan, and it will save us some work. You already wrote the 10th multiple, 410. How big would the 20th multiple of 41 be?

Students might say:

"It's twice as much. So it's 820."

Count up to where the 20th multiple should be and write 820. Then keep going and write the 21st, 22nd, and 23rd multiples. Be sure students understand that the 23rd multiple, 943, is the solution to the problem.

Next, have pairs of students use multiple towers to find 32 × 52. Emphasize the efficiency of finding the 10th, 20th, and 30th multiples. You might want to suggest how to keep track of the skipped multiples, as shown at the right. Point out that this simplifies the work and saves space.

32nd	1,664
31st	1,612
30th	1,560
.	
.	
.	
20th	1,040
.	
.	
10th	520
	468
	416
	364
	312
5th	260
	208
	156
	104
1st	52

Have students share any new shortcuts they've discovered, such as doubling the 5th multiple to find the 10th multiple.

Some students might be ready to use the 10th, 20th, 30th multiples, and so on, to solve other problems without actually drawing multiple towers.

(**ELL**) **English Language Learners**

Use Repetition Review the meaning of the word *multiple*. Emphasize the word as you ask repeated questions about the multiple tower. For example: What is the 10th *multiple* of 41? What is the 20th *multiple* of 41?

Additional Resource

Student Math Handbook page 36

Practice

20 MIN   PAIRS

Picturing Multiplication Problems

Use anytime after Session 1.5.

Math Focus Points

◆ Solving 2-digit multiplication problems by breaking a problem into smaller parts and combining the subproducts

◆ Multiplying multiples of 10

◆ Using a story problem represented by a multiplication expression to keep track of parts of the problem

Materials: R74

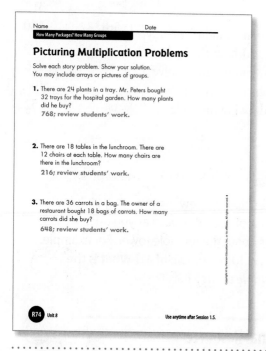

Read this story problem to students: The owner of a restaurant bought 36 boxes of straws. There are 48 straws in a box. How many straws did she buy?

How can you show this problem using an array or a picture of groups? Have volunteers sketch examples.

If you want to use a picture, remember you may not have to draw every group or every object. Just draw enough so you can keep track.

Students might say:

"I made an array. It shows each of the factors in the problem broken up into tens and ones."

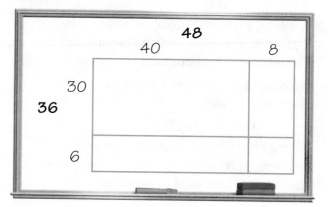

Work in pairs to solve the problem using your array or picture of groups. What smaller multiplication problems will you solve? How can you use the answers to the smaller problems to find 48 × 36? Have students share their methods. Ask students to relate each smaller part of their solution to part of the original story problem about boxes of straws.

How can you break the problem into parts without a drawing? Work in pairs. Show how to solve the problem using just numbers. Ask volunteers to explain their work.

Distribute copies of Picturing Multiplication Problems (R74).

> **ELL** **English Language Learners**
>
> **Provide Sentence Stems** To help students explain how to multiply by tens and ones, provide sentence stems. For example: First, break 36 into _____ (30 + 6), and break 48 into _____ (40 + 8). Next, multiply _____ (30 by 40 and 30 by 8). Then, multiply _____ (6 by 40 and 6 by 8). Finally, _____ (add all the answers).

Additional Resource

Student Math Handbook page 41

Extension

Cluster Problems

Use anytime after Session 1.3.

Math Focus Points

◆ Solving 2-digit multiplication problems by breaking a problem into smaller parts and combining the subproducts

◆ Multiplying by multiples of 10

Materials: R75

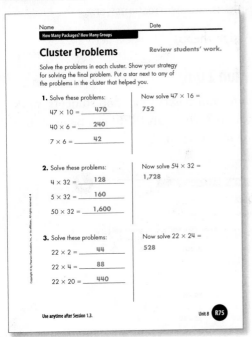

Students might say:

 "We think it would help to break apart 62 into 60 + 2 and multiply each part by 23. So our cluster has 60 × 20 and 60 × 3. That takes care of 60 × 23. You still have to multiply 2 × 23, so we added that to the cluster."

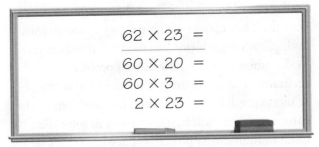

$$62 \times 23 =$$
$$60 \times 20 =$$
$$60 \times 3 =$$
$$2 \times 23 =$$

Have students compare the various clusters offered by students. Do you like some clusters better than others? Why? Are there any problems you would change in your cluster to make a better cluster of problems?

Have pairs write a multiplication problem with two 2-digit factors as well as a cluster of problems to help solve it. Collect the papers and redistribute them. Ask each pair to solve the cluster problems and the final problem they are given. Then distribute copies of Cluster Problems (R75).

Today you will work with your partner to create a cluster of problems that another pair can use to solve a problem. Let's start by thinking of what makes helpful problems. What cluster of problems would help solve this problem? Write 62 × 23 = on the board.

As students suggest clusters of problems, record them on the board. Point to individual problems and ask: How does this problem help solve the final problem? How does it work together with the other problems to lead to a solution?

ELL **English Language Learners**

Partner Talk Listen as partners discuss how the different problems in the cluster help solve the final problem. Are students able to verbalize which parts can be used to solve the final problem? Beginner English Language Learners may only be able to respond with short phrases or point to their work and use gestures. Step in, as needed, and ask leading questions that will encourage students to put their thinking into words.

Additional Resource

Student Math Handbook page 39

Differentiation in Investigation 2

Mathematics in This Investigation

The mathematics focuses on solving 2-digit by 2-digit multiplication problems using different strategies.

Additional Resource: *Breaking Numbers Apart to Solve 2-Digit Multiplication Problems*, pages 115–116 (See Curriculum Unit 8)

Understanding the Mathematics

Students multiply 2-digit by 2-digit numbers fluently. They choose which strategy to use to solve multiplication problems based on the numbers given in the problem. They solve related problems accurately and use them to solve the final problem. Students are able to choose which expressions in the cluster problems will best help them to solve the given multiplication problem. They keep track of what parts of the problem they have solved and what remains to be solved. Students may solve multiplication problems by changing one factor to create an easier problem.

Option: Assign the Extension activity.

Partially Understanding the Mathematics

Students understand the operation of multiplication, but they are working at becoming more efficient and accurate with multiplying 2-digit by 2-digit numbers. They use one strategy to solve multiplication problems. Students solve related problems and cluster problems, but they do not see the relationship between the solutions in those problems and the solution to the final problem. They may break numbers apart in less than efficient ways (e.g., breaking 34 into 10 + 10 + 10 + 4), and they are likely to have trouble keeping track of what parts of the problem they have solved and what remains.

Option: Assign the Practice activity.

Not Understanding the Mathematics

Students are unable to solve most 2-digit multiplication problems. Difficulties include failing to multiply all the partial products, multiplying incorrectly, and losing track of the different parts. Students might be using repeated addition to solve problems. They see related problems and cluster problems as individual problems, and they do not see how solving them individually relates to solving the final problem. They only use one strategy, which usually results in an incorrect answer.

Option: Assign the Intervention activity.

Investigation 2 Quiz

In addition to your observations and students' work in Investigation 2, the Quiz (R76) can be used to gather more information.

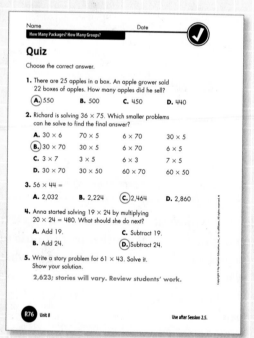

Intervention

20 MIN   PAIRS

Organizing Subproducts

Use anytime after Session 2.4.

Math Focus Points

◆ Solving 2-digit multiplication problems by breaking a problem into smaller parts and combining the subproducts

◆ Multiplying by multiples of 10

Write 27 × 34 on the board. Have students help you break 27 and 34 into tens and ones and write the parts along the sides of an array. For this activity, it's important to show the array mostly to scale.

When you break a problem into parts by tens and ones, you have to multiply each part of one number by each part of the other number. You can keep track of this with a diagram and by thinking of a story context. Suppose there are 27 classrooms in a school, and each room has 34 students. Take one rectangle at a time and draw arrows to show students which numbers to write as factors. Have students come to the board to write the factors.

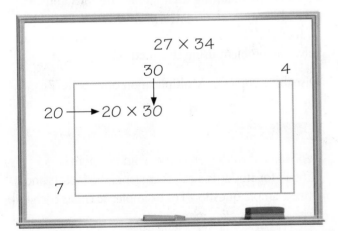

Have students follow the diagram to write and solve the four multiplication problems shown in the array. For each partial product, ask students to identify what part of the problem they have solved and how the numbers connect to the context. Ask questions such as, What's the 20? Have we accounted for all the classrooms? All the students? Then have them solve the original problem.

Can anyone show a different way to organize the parts so you can be sure you don't skip any of them? Are your parts in the same order? Does it matter?

Students might say:

 "After you write the tens and ones, you could draw arrows from each part of 27 to each part of 34. Then write one problem for each arrow. My parts are in a different order, but the answer is the same."

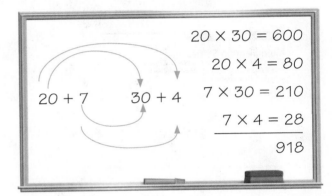

Have pairs select one of the methods discussed in the activity and use it to solve 43 × 32.

ELL English Language Learners

Use Repetition As you ask students about each subproduct, structure the questions the same way. For example: First, multiply 20 by which number? Next, multiply 20 by which number? Then, multiply 7 by which number? Finally, multiply 7 by which number?

Additional Resource

Student Math Handbook page 41

Practice

25 MIN **PAIRS**

Multiplication Stories

Use anytime after Session 2.4.

Math Focus Points

◆ Solving 2-digit multiplication problems by changing one factor to create an easier problem

◆ Solving 2-digit multiplication problems by breaking a problem into smaller parts and combining the subproducts

◆ Multiplying by multiples of 10

Materials: R77

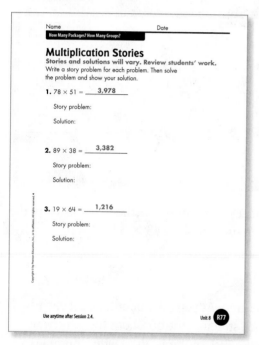

Write $39 \times 86 =$ on the board. Have pairs work together to write a story problem for the problem. Ask students to share their stories.

Students might say:

"A furniture factory made 86 chairs a week for 39 weeks. How many chairs were made?"

Let's try some different ways to find the answer. What if you start by changing 39 to 40 and finding 40×86? How much is that? How can you finish the problem?

Students might say:

"You get 3,440. Then you have to subtract 86 because you multiplied one too many 86s."

Show the completed equations on the board.

$$40 \times 86 = 3,440$$
$$3,440 - 86 = 3,354$$

What does each of these equations mean in terms of [Jake's] story about the furniture factory?

Students might say:

"The first equation tells how many chairs were made in 40 weeks. In the second equation, you take off the 86 chairs for the extra week."

Let's try another way to solve this problem. What if you start by breaking each factor into tens and ones? What are the smaller problems you can solve to find the final answer? Have students show how to solve the problem using this method.

Distribute copies of Multiplication Stories (R77).

ELL English Language Learners

Rephrase If writing an entire word problem is difficult for students, have them label the factors and write a simple question. For example: *86 chairs each week, 39 weeks. How many in all?*

Additional Resource

Student Math Handbook pages 40–43

Extension

25 MIN   PAIRS

Multiplying 3-Digit Numbers

Use anytime after Session 2.4.

Math Focus Points

◆ Solving 2-digit multiplication problems by changing one factor to create an easier problem

◆ Solving 2-digit multiplication problems by breaking a problem into smaller parts and combining the subproducts

◆ Multiplying by multiples of 10

Materials: R78

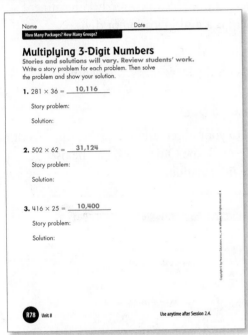

How can you break this problem into smaller parts?

Students might say:

 "Break 346 into 300 + 40 + 6 and 52 into 50 + 2. Multiply 300 × 50, 40 × 50, 6 × 50, and 300 × 2, 40 × 2, 6 × 2. Then add all the answers."

Let's look at other ways to solve the problem. What could we do with the 52? Students might suggest breaking 52 into 50 and 2. They would multiply 346 × 50 and add 2 × 346.

What cluster of problems can you think of to help you solve the problem? Have students suggest some clusters of problems and show how they can be used to find the final answer.

Distribute copies of Multiplying 3-Digit Numbers (R78).

ELL **English Language Learners**

Provide a Word List Review the words *hundreds*, *tens*, and *ones*. Then use these words to help students break numbers apart. For example: The number 346 has how many *hundreds*? It has how many *tens*? It has how many *ones*?

Additional Resource

Student Math Handbook pages 40–43

You have learned a number of ways to multiply 2-digit numbers by 2-digit numbers. You can use some of the same methods to multiply 3-digit numbers by 2-digit numbers.

Write 346 × 52 = on the board. Work with your partner to make up a story problem for this multiplication problem. Have students share their stories.

Differentiation in Investigation 3

Mathematics in This Investigation

The mathematics focuses on using the relationship between multiplication and division to solve division problems.

Understanding the Mathematics

Students solve division problems efficiently by using either multiplication or division, often using the biggest "chunks" of numbers. They keep track of all parts of the problem and use clear and concise notation in their answers. Students see and use relationships of multiples of 10 and other landmark multiples (e.g., 5th, 20th) to solve problems. They correctly interpret story problems as either a multiplication or division situation.

Option: Assign the Extension activity.

Partially Understanding the Mathematics

Students understand what the operation of division is, but they have difficulty in consistently and efficiently solving division problems accurately. They understand and use the relationship between multiplication and division. They may break the numbers into too many parts and struggle to keep track of all of their work. They understand how the 10th multiple of a number helps them solve division problems, but they don't necessarily see the relationship of other multiples. Students usually are able to determine if a story problem is a multiplication or division situation.

Option: Assign the Practice activity.

Not Understanding the Mathematics

Students may understand what the operation of division is. To solve division problems, however, they rely on using materials and counting either the number of groups or the number in one group. They only consider one group at a time, rather than considering how using multiples of that number would help them solve the problem more efficiently and accurately. Students might be able to solve problems correctly using tools or drawings, but then they have difficulty knowing what the answer is and using notation to communicate their solution. Students may not be able to correctly determine if a story problem is a multiplication or division situation.

Option: Assign the Intervention activity.

Investigation 3 Quiz

In addition to your observations and students' work in Investigation 3, the Quiz (R79) can be used to gather more information.

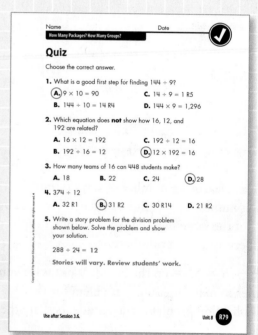

Intervention

20 MIN   INDIVIDUALS

Division Strategies

Use anytime after Session 3.4.

Math Focus Points

◆ Using multiples of 10 to solve division problems

◆ Solving division problems by breaking the problem into parts

◆ Using a story problem represented by a division expression to keep track of parts of the problem

Write the following problem on the board and read it out loud. You have 420 stickers. There are 30 stickers on a sheet. How many sheets of stickers do you have?

Ask each student to write the division problem that represents the sticker story. How many stickers are on 10 sheets? How many stickers would be on the rest of the sheets? As you ask these questions, help students record the corresponding equations.

$420 \div 30 =$

$10 \times 30 = 300$
$420 - 300 = 120$

Could there be another 10 sheets for these 120 stickers? How do you know?

Students might say:

"There aren't enough stickers for another 10 sheets. 10 sheets of 30 is 300 stickers."

Could there be another 2 sheets? How do you know? As students answer the questions, continue to help them record the corresponding equations. Guide them once again to consider how many stickers are unaccounted for, and help them continue working until all the stickers are accounted for. Tell

students to identify the number of sheets in each part of the problem so they can figure out the total number of sheets.

$420 \div 30 =$

$10 \times 30 = 300$ 10 sheets
$420 - 300 = 120$

$2 \times 30 = 60$ 2 sheets
$120 - 60 = 60$

$2 \times 30 = 60$ 2 sheets
$60 - 60 = 0$

$420 \div 30 = 14$ 14 sheets in all

Pose another problem, this time with 690 stickers. Guide students to understand that they can make another group of 10 sheets after accounting for the first group.

ELL English Language Learners

Rephrase Rephrase the word problems as needed. You might need to rephrase *sheet* as *page*, or hold up a sheet of paper. Ask students to draw a picture of *30 stickers on a sheet* to show that they understand.

Additional Resource

Student Math Handbook pages 44–45

Practice

20 MIN **PAIRS**

Stories for Division
Use anytime after Session 3.3.

Math Focus Points

◆ Using multiples of 10 to solve division problems

◆ Solving division problems by breaking the problem into parts

◆ Using a story problem represented by a division expression to keep track of parts of the problem

Materials: R80

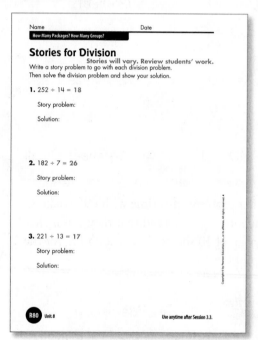

Write $414 \div 18 =$ on the board.

Work with your partner. What story problem can you write for this division problem?

Students might say:

"A CD case holds 18 CDs. How many CD cases are needed to hold 414 CDs?"

Discuss some methods students might use to find how many 18s there are in 414. Have students work

in pairs to solve the problem. As students work, ask questions such as the following:

◆ How can you use multiples of 10 to help you solve the division problem?

◆ Can you break the problem into parts to help you find the answer?

When students are finished, have them share their solutions and relate the numbers in their solutions to their story problem.

Students might say:

"We found $10 \times 18 = 180$, so 10 cases hold 180 CDs. Then we doubled that. 20 cases hold 360 CDs. Then 2×18 is 36, so 22 cases hold 396 CDs and 23 cases hold 414 CDs. So $414 \div 18 = 23$."

$$414 \div 18 =$$
$$10 \times 18 = 180$$
$$20 \times 18 = 360$$
$$2 \times 18 = 36$$
$$\overline{22 \times 18 = 396}$$
$$1 \times 18 = 18$$
$$\overline{23 \times 18 = 414}$$

Distribute copies of Stories for Division (R80).

⬤ **ELL** ⬤ **English Language Learners**

Use Repetition Encourage all students to take part explaining how the steps of their solution relate to the story. Remind students to look at the story and repeat back the important words (e.g., *CDs, cases*) as they give their explanations.

Additional Resource

Student Math Handbook pages 45, 50–52

20 MIN   **PAIRS**

Extension

Dividing with Larger Numbers

Use anytime after Session 3.1.

Math Focus Points

◆ Solving division problems by breaking the problem into parts

◆ Representing a multiplication or division problem with pictures or diagrams, including arrays and pictures of groups

◆ Using a story problem represented by a division expression to keep track of parts of the problem

Materials: R81

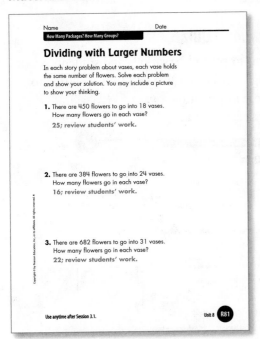

Write the following problem on the board.

There are 864 students at Kennedy High School. How many groups of 36 students can the principal make?

Have students work in pairs to solve the problem. As they work, ask questions such as the following:

◆ Do you think there will be more or fewer than 20 groups? Why?

◆ Will there be more or fewer than 30 groups? How do you know?

Students might say:

"There will be more than 20 groups because 20 × 36 = 720. There will be fewer than 30 groups because 30 × 36 = 1,080."

When students have finished, have pairs share their methods for solving the problem. Students may use multiplication or division equations.

Students might say:

"We started with 20 × 36 = 720. We subtracted that from 864 and it was 144. So we did 2 × 36 = 72 and subtracted again, and got 72! We knew it was 2 more groups of 36. So the 864 students can be split into 24 groups of 36."

Work together to try another one. How many groups of 42 can 756 people make? Have students share and discuss their solutions. Then distribute copies of Dividing with Larger Numbers (R81).

(**ELL**) English Language Learners

Model Thinking Aloud   You may want to verbalize the relationship between multiplication and division for the first problem. Write 864 ÷ 36 = 24 and 24 × 36 = 864 on the board. Point to the parts of the multiplication and division equation as you model aloud. Divide 864 by 36 to get 24. Multiply 24 times 36 to get 864. Then have students do the same for the second problem.

Additional Resource

Student Math Handbook pages 50–52

Differentiation in Investigation 1

Mathematics in This Investigation

The mathematics focuses on using graphs to represent change in time and speed. The math also focuses on matching graphs to written descriptions.

Additional Resource: *Using Line Graphs to Represent Change*, pages 133–137 (See Curriculum Unit 9)

Understanding the Mathematics

Students create graphs that accurately display change in temperature or speed. They interpret the points and shape of a graph in terms of the situation the graph represents (e.g., higher points indicate hotter temperatures and lower points indicate cooler temperatures). When reading and creating speed graphs, students match the descriptions to corresponding graphs, correctly interpreting slanted portions of the graph as representing a change in speed, and level sections of the graph as representing a steady speed. Students correctly interpret the speed at zero to mean a stoppage in movement.

Option: Assign the Extension activity.

Partially Understanding the Mathematics

Students' graphs are generally correct in displaying the change in temperature or speed. While they can place the data on the graph accurately, students may not understand how the graph relates to different situations (e.g., speeding up or slowing down). Their speed graphs usually match the descriptions, but they may sometimes read a level section as a stoppage in movement rather than maintaining speed. Students may not always interpret the speed graph at zero to mean a stoppage in movement.

Option: Assign the Practice activity.

Not Understanding the Mathematics

Students have difficulty interpreting graphs that do not have numbers on the *x*- and *y*-axes. Students' graphs do not correctly display the change in temperature or a change in speed. Students have difficulty explaining how a graph shows a change in temperature or a change in speed. They do not make the connection between high and low points on the graph and either high and low temperatures or fast and slow speeds. Their speed graphs do not match the descriptions for change in speed. Students do not correctly interpret the graph at zero.

Option: Assign the Intervention activity.

Investigation 1 Quiz

In addition to your observations and students' work in Investigation 1, the Quiz (R82) can be used to gather more information.

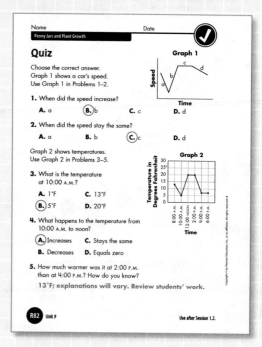

Intervention

20 MIN **PAIRS**

Graphs for Speed

Use anytime after Session 1.1.

Math Focus Points

◆ Interpreting the points and shape of a graph in terms of the situation the graph represents

Vocabulary: speed, graph

Materials: small toy cars

. . . .

Use a small toy car to model a car trip. Move the car along on a table or desk as you describe its speed. My car is moving along at the same speed. Now it stops. Now it speeds up.

Draw Graphs 1 and 2 on the board.

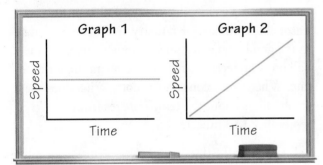

These graphs tell different stories about the speed of the car. What is happening in Graph 1? Graph 2? Who can show us with the toy car? Stress the fact that a flat line does not mean the car has stopped. It means that the speed of the car is not changing.

Draw Graphs 3 and 4.

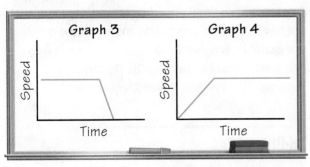

Have students describe what is happening to the speed of the cars in Graphs 3 and 4. Ask students to use the toy cars to model what each graph shows.

Letters can be used to name the parts of the graph. Who can tell me what is happening in each part on these graphs? Draw Graphs 5 and 6.

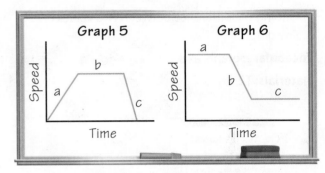

Students might say:

 "In Graph 5, the car speeds up in part a. Then in part b, it drives at the same speed. In part c, it slows down and stops."

 "In Graph 6, the car is going at the same speed in part a. In part b, it slows down. Then it drives at the same speed in part c, but it is going slower than in part a."

Have pairs take turns making little car trips with the toy cars to model what is shown in Graphs 5 and 6.

ELL **English Language Learners**

Provide Sentence Stems To help students describe the situations shown in the graphs, provide sentence stems. For example: In part A the car _____. In part B the car _____. In Part C the car _____.

Additional Resource

Student Math Handbook pages 75–76

Practice

25 MIN   GROUPS

City Temperatures

Use anytime after Session 1.1.

Math Focus Points

◆ Interpreting the points and shape of a graph in terms of the situation the graph represents

◆ Finding the difference between two values on a line graph

Vocabulary: graph, axis

Materials: T2, R83

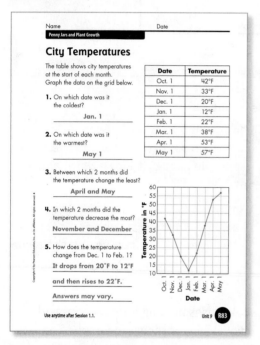

Ask students to think about how the temperature in degrees Fahrenheit changes during the school year in your area. Today we will make a graph that shows temperatures from September to June. What are the coldest and hottest temperatures you can remember? In which months did those temperatures occur?

Students might say:

"I think it is always the coldest in January. I can remember it was 10 degrees below zero."

Begin this graph on the transparency for One-Centimeter Grid Paper (T2). Number the vertical axis by 5s, starting with 5 degrees below the coldest temperature your students remember.

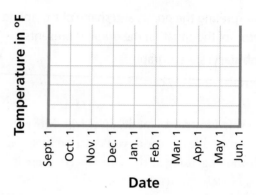

What does each axis on the graph show? On which date do we have the coldest days? What is a reasonable estimate for January 1? Discuss each date on the graph and agree on a reasonable temperature. Call on volunteers to graph the temperature for each date. When done, connect the dots. What does the graph tell us about the temperatures from September 1 to June 1?

Students might say:

"As you move from left to right on the graph, the temperatures go down and then back up."

Distribute copies of City Temperatures (R83).

> **ELL** **English Language Learners**

Rephrase Ask simple but direct questions to help students verbalize generalizations about the graph. For example: When is it the coldest? When is it the warmest? What happens to the temperature between [September] 1 and [December] 1?

Additional Resource

Student Math Handbook pages 72–74

Extension

25 MIN PAIRS

Speed Graphs

Use anytime after Session 1.2.

Math Focus Points

◆ Interpreting the points and shape of a graph in terms of the situation the graph represents

Vocabulary: graph

Materials: T87, R84

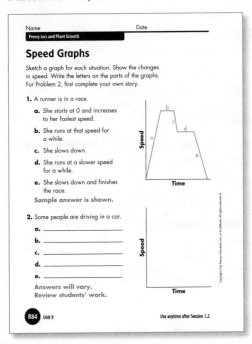

You can write a story from a line graph. But you can also do the reverse. You can use a story to make a graph. You did this for the wheelchair racer in the Boston Marathon. I'll tell a story, and you sketch the graph.

I drove my car to the store. I slowly increased my speed to 30 miles per hour, drove for 15 minutes at a steady speed, and then stopped. Have students mark the three parts of the trip with the letters a, b, and c. Students' graphs might look like this:

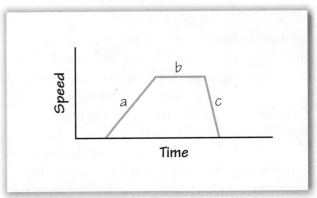

Ask each student to make up a similar story about a moving object. Have his or her partner sketch a graph to represent the story. Then distribute copies of Speed Graphs (R84).

Display The Motion Graph (T87). You have used this graph to tell stories about a runner in a race. But the graph does not have to be about a runner. It can be about any moving object. What are some moving objects this graph could describe?

Students might say:

"It could be about people on a car trip. They start out, go faster, go the same speed a little while and then stop for a little while. Maybe they stopped for lunch—or they had a flat tire!"

"The flat parts of the graph show times when the speed isn't changing. It could be an airplane. It goes up to its flying altitude and stays at that same speed."

Provide a Word List Make a three-column chart to describe ways speed can change. Head the columns: *Faster, Slower, Stays the Same*. Work with students to list other words for each column. A sample is shown.

Faster	Slower	Stays the Same
increases	decreases	steady
goes up	goes down	doesn't change
speeds up	slows down	

Additional Resource

Student Math Handbook pages 75–76

Differentiation in Investigation 2

Mathematics in This Investigation

The mathematics focuses on describing and representing different situations of constant change using tables, graphs, words, and symbolic notation.

Additional Resources: *Representing a Constant Rate of Change*, pages 140–142 (See Curriculum Unit 9); *Helping Students Make Sense of Penny Jar Problems: Using an Array Representation*, pages 89–91 (See *Implementing Investigations in Grade 4*)

Understanding the Mathematics

Students correctly interpret different situations involving Penny Jars or Windows and Towers. They create representations that show the change over a period of time using tables and graphs. They accurately describe how their representations show a starting point, amount added each round, and the total. They determine the totals for future rounds without counting each individual round, and they write arithmetic expressions using multiplication and addition to calculate those totals. Students also begin to articulate a general rule and may write expressions that include a variable.

Option: Assign the Extension activity.

Partially Understanding the Mathematics

Students use representations to show the change over time in situations involving Penny Jars or Windows and Towers. However, they may have difficulty matching tables to their corresponding graphs. They can explain the graphs correctly and describe the changes in the graph, but they are still developing strategies for determining future rounds accurately. Students count out the amount for each round and then create arithmetic expressions using multiplication and addition. They can associate individual rules for given situations, but not a general rule to cover all instances.

Option: Assign the Practice activity.

Not Understanding the Mathematics

Students do not understand how to represent change over time using tables or graphs to display the situations involving Penny Jars or Windows and Towers. Through direct modeling, they determine the total for each round, but they do not make connections to future rounds. They need a visual representation to support their thinking when starting at one point and adding a certain number to show change. Students struggle to explain the total number of pennies or windows and to display their results through a representation.

Option: Assign the Intervention activity.

Investigation 2 Quiz

In addition to your observations and students' work in Investigation 2, the Quiz (R85) can be used to gather more information.

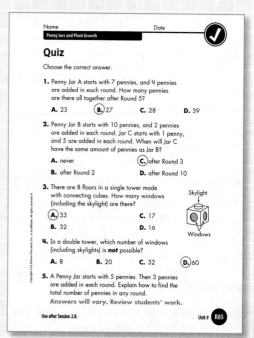

Intervention

25 MIN   INDIVIDUALS

Color Tiles and Penny Jars
Use anytime after Session 2.3.

Math Focus Points

◆ Finding the value of one quantity in a situation of constant change, given the value of the other (e.g., if you know the number of the round, what is the total number of pennies?)

Vocabulary: table, round

Materials: color tiles or pennies, blank paper, M20 (2 per student)

. . . .

Distribute color tiles (or use pennies) and copies of Penny Jar Table (M20). Today we'll pretend these tiles are pennies. For Situation A, we'll start with 0 tiles and add 2 red tiles in each round. Help students label a sheet of paper as shown below. Then have them display the tiles through Round 4.

Situation A

Start with 0. Add 2 each round.

Start with 0

Round 1   ▉ ▉

Round 2   ▉ ▉

Round 3   ▉ ▉

Round 4   ▉ ▉

How many tiles are there altogether after Round 1? After Round 2? Round 3? Round 4? Can you tell how many there will be after Round 5 without actually placing the tiles? Have students record the number of tiles through Round 5 on M20. What pattern do you see in the table? Ask students how they can figure out how many tiles there will be after the 10th round.

Have students carefully slide Situation A aside and prepare another sheet for Situation B. This time

students start with 3 blue tiles and add 2 red tiles in each round.

Situation B

Start with 3. Add 2 each round.

Start with 3   ▉ ▉ ▉

Round 1   ▉ ▉

Round 2   ▉ ▉

Round 3   ▉ ▉

Round 4   ▉ ▉

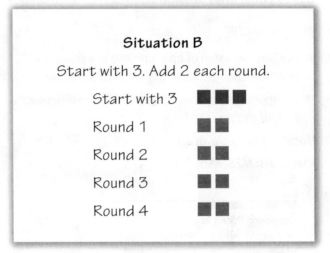

Discuss the total number of tiles after each round. On another copy of M20, have students complete the table through Round 5 and look for a pattern. How can you figure out how many tiles there will be after the 10th round? How does this compare to the 10th round in Situation A?

Students might say:

"In Situation A, you can skip count by 2s. You can do the same in Situation B, but then you have to add 3 because we started with 3 tiles."

Carefully compare the two situations. Be sure students see that after *every* round, there are always 3 more tiles in Situation B than in Situation A because Situation B starts with 3 tiles. Connect this with "adding 3."

(**ELL**) **English Language Learners**

Rephrase Help students understand the idea of a *round* by using more familiar words such as *step* or *turn*.

Additional Resource

Student Math Handbook pages 79–80

Practice

30 MIN   GROUPS

Comparing Penny Jars

Use anytime after Session 2.5.

Math Focus Points

◆ Finding the value of one quantity in a situation of constant change, given the value of the other

◆ Comparing situations by describing the differences in their graphs

Vocabulary: table, graph

Materials: M28–M29, R86

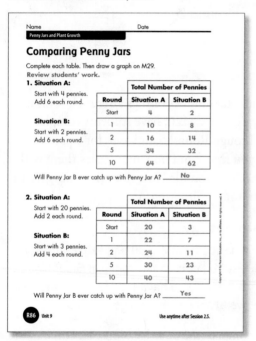

Have students work in groups of three. Each member should complete the table and graph on Penny Jar Comparisons (M28–M29). One group member should work on Situation A and Situation B1, as given in the plan shown. Another group member should work on Situation A and Situation B2. The third group member should work on Situation A and Situation B3.

> **A:** Start with 6 pennies.
>   Add 5 pennies each round.
>
> **B1:** Start with 2 pennies.
>   Add 7 pennies each round.
>
> **B2:** Start with 2 pennies.
>   Add 4 pennies each round.
>
> **B3:** Start with 2 pennies.
>   Add 5 pennies each round.

Have students compare their results. Jars B1, B2, and B3 all started with fewer pennies than Jar A. Does B1, B2, or B3 ever catch up to A? How can you tell from the graph?

Students might say:

"Only B1 catches up. In Round 2, A and B1 have the same total number of pennies. After that, B1 always has more. In the graph, the line for B1 starts lower, but it crosses A at 2 rounds and then stays higher than A."

Suppose you were to start again with 8 pennies in Jar A and 3 pennies in Jar B. How can Jar B catch up? Some students might realize that Jar B will always catch up and pass Jar A if there are more pennies per round being added to Jar B.

Distribute copies of Comparing Penny Jars (R86). Students will need to use M29 to complete R86.

(**ELL**) **English Language Learners**

Rephrase Be sure students understand the concept of *catch up*. You might want to rephrase this as *have the same number of pennies*.

Additional Resource

Student Math Handbook pages 82–85

Extension

20 MIN   PAIRS

Bigger Penny Jars

Use anytime after Session 2.4.

Math Focus Points

◆ Plotting points on a coordinate grid to represent a situation in which one quantity is changing in relation to another

Vocabulary: graph, scale

Materials: M2 (from Unit 1; 2 per student), T2, R87

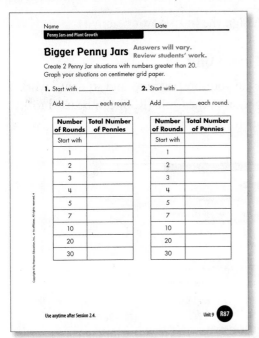

On the board, draw a table following the format shown on *Student Activity Book* page 27. Imagine a Penny Jar situation with greater numbers. Let's say you started with 20 pennies and then add 40 pennies in each round. Call on volunteers to record the data in the table.

Display the transparency of One-Centimeter Graph Paper (T2). Now, let's make a graph for 12 rounds of this Penny Jar situation. How high would you want the numbers to go on the scale that shows the number of pennies?

Students might say:

"If we add 40 each time, that would be 480. Plus 20 that we started with. The scale would need to go to at least 500."

Work with students to set up the graph on the transparency. Discuss reasonable ways to number the vertical scale. Call on volunteers to plot the data for Rounds 1 through 12.

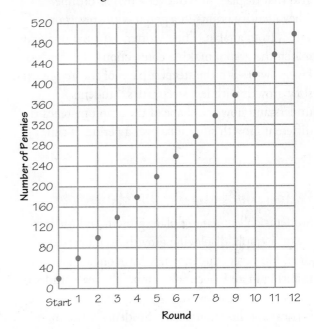

Distribute copies of Bigger Penny Jars (R87). Each student will need 2 copies of M2 to complete R87.

ELL   **English Language Learners**

Use Repetition Ask direct questions to help students decide how to plot each point. For example: How many pennies are there altogether after 4 rounds? How many pennies are there altogether after 5 rounds?

Additional Resource

Student Math Handbook page 81

Differentiation in Investigation 3

Mathematics in This Investigation

The mathematics focuses on making graphs and describing the change the graph represents. The work also focuses on matching graphs with tables and stories.

Understanding the Mathematics

Students accurately collect and use data about the growth of plants to create graphs on a coordinate grid that display growth over a period of time. They identify points in a graph with corresponding values from a table. Their written explanations match the graph, making connections of periods of fast growth with the steepest parts of the graphs, and slow growth with less steep parts. Students understand how the shape of the graph matches the different growth situations over a period of time.

Option: Assign the Extension activity.

Partially Understanding the Mathematics

Students collect data of plant growth and use it to create a graph, displaying growth over a period of time. However, students may leave out some data, resulting in an inaccurate graph. The scale students use may not be consistent, or they may mix up the vertical and horizontal axes. Students' written explanations generally match the graph with a few inconsistencies. Students understand how the shapes of various graphs match different situations, but they may not understand how a more leveled section of a graph corresponds to little growth over a period of time.

Option: Assign the Practice activity.

Not Understanding the Mathematics

Students plot points correctly on a graph, but they do not understand how the steepness in a section of the graph relates to how quickly the plant grew over a certain period of time. The scales on the graph are not consistent with the range of the data. Students' written descriptions do not match the graphs. They have difficulty interpreting graphs and do not understand how the shapes of various graphs connect to different situations.

Option: Assign the Intervention activity.

Investigation 3 Quiz

In addition to your observations and students' work in Investigation 3, the Quiz (R88) can be used to gather more information.

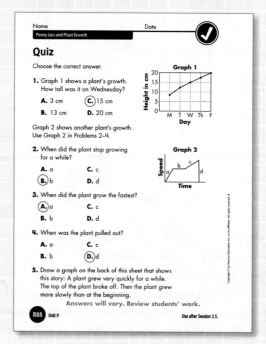

Intervention

25 MIN   INDIVIDUALS

Making Plant Graphs

Use anytime after Session 3.3.

Math Focus Points

◆ Identifying points in a graph with corresponding values in a table and interpreting the numerical information in terms of the situation the graph represents

Vocabulary: graph

Materials: R89

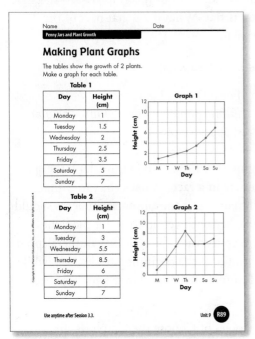

Tell students they will make graphs that show the height of two growing plants over a one-week period. Distribute copies of Making Plant Graphs (R89). Discuss how the axes are labeled. Be sure students understand that the interval on the vertical axis is numbered in 2s. Work with students as they plot the first several points in Graph 1. Check that they know how to show a height that is not a whole number, such as 1.5 cm. Have students finish plotting the seven points in Graph 1. Then have them join the points.

Show me on the graph where the plant was growing slowly. Where was the plant growing faster? Be sure students understand that the steeper parts of the graph represent faster growth. Did the plant ever "rest" and not grow at all? How can you tell from the graph?

Students might say:

"The graph keeps going up and up. The points get higher and higher, so that means the plant is getting higher and higher. It never took a rest."

Have students complete Graph 2. Show me on the graph where the plant was growing steadily. Show me on the graph where the plant was the tallest. What do you think might have happened between Thursday and Friday?

Students might say:

"The plant got shorter. So maybe someone cut the top off."

Show me on the graph where the plant didn't grow for a while. Then what happened after that?

ELL **English Language Learners**

Provide a Word List Talk with students and generate a list of phrases related to changes in growth. For example, for rapid increases in height, students might suggest *growing fast* or *growing quickly*. Have students refer to their list to help them understand and take part in the discussions about the plant-growth graphs.

Additional Resource

Student Math Handbook page 77

Practice

20 MIN   GROUPS

Choose the Graph

Use anytime after Session 3.4.

Math Focus Points

◆ Interpreting the points and shape of a graph in terms of the situation the graph represents

Vocabulary: graph

Materials: R90

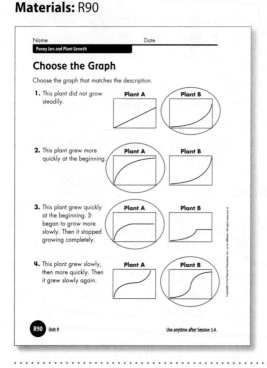

. . . .

Here are two graphs that show how something changes over time. Sketch these graphs on the board.

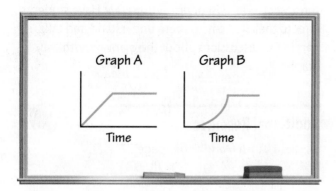

How are the graphs the same? How are they different? What is missing from both graphs? Work

in your group and make up a story that might match the shape of each graph. Ask groups to share their stories. Discuss whether the stories offered are a good match for the graphs.

Suppose I told you that one graph shows a Penny Jar situation and one shows a plant's height. Which is which? Remind students that plants usually do not show steady growth. Graph A is likely the Penny Jar situation. The part with the steady increase represents when the same number of pennies are added each round. Both of the graphs have a section that is flat. What does that part of the graph represent?

Students might say:

"For a Penny Jar, it means we stopped adding pennies. For a plant, the plant stopped growing."

Now imagine that these two graphs show the speed of two runners in a race. What's the same and what's different about the runners? Students should suggest that they both get up to about the same speed and keep it steady. But the first runner's speed increases steadily at the beginning of the race, while the second runner starts out slower and gets faster and faster.

Distribute copies of Choose the Graph (R90).

⬤ **ELL** ⬤ **English Language Learners**

Rephrase Some students may confuse the *shape* of a graph with the use of *shape* to designate polygons and circles in geometry. The shape of a graph is the *path* that the graph shows. It might have straight parts, curves, and bends. It might go up, go down, or stay flat.

_____

Additional Resource

Student Math Handbook pages 75–77

Extension

20 MIN   PAIRS

Comparing Increasing and Decreasing Situations

Use anytime after Session 3.4.

Math Focus Points

◆ Writing an arithmetic expression for finding the value of one quantity in terms of the other in a situation of constant change

Vocabulary: increasing, decreasing

Materials: M28

. . . .

Distribute a copy of Penny Jar Comparisons (M28) to each student. Let's say Jar A starts with 170 pennies and 8 pennies are added each round. Have students record this for Situation A. Jar B starts with 170 pennies and 8 pennies are taken out each round. Have students record this for Situation B, changing "Add" to "Subtract." Then have them complete the table through Round 5.

Talk to your partner. Try to find a rule for Situation A that will tell you how many pennies there are for any round. Then use your rule to figure out how many pennies will be in Jar A after the 20th round.

Students might say:

"We multiplied the number of the round by 8 and added it to 170. So that's 330 pennies after the 20th round."

"We got the same answer. But we used the letter r for the number of the round and we wrote $170 + (r \times 8)$."

If no one suggests the expression, bring it up yourself and write it on the board. Remind students that the parentheses tell them to multiply before they add. To verify that the expression "works," have students substitute 4 for r and compare the value of the expression to the value they gave in the table for Round 4.

What rule could you use for Situation B? How can you write it as an expression with the letter r? Use your rule to find how many pennies will be in Jar B after the 20th round.

Students might say:

"You have to multiply the number of the round by 8 and subtract that from 170, so we wrote $170 - (r \times 8)$. There are 10 pennies after Round 20."

Write the expression for Situation B under the one for Situation A. Have students verify that the second expression "works" by substituting 4 for r.

Penny Jar A $170 + (r \times 8)$

Penny Jar B $170 - (r \times 8)$

Again, discuss what the parentheses indicate. Then, have students use the rules to help them complete all the rows of the table on M28.

What's the same and what's different about the rules? Which rule is for an increasing Penny Jar situation? Which rule is for a decreasing Penny Jar situation? How can you look at the rules and tell which is which?

If time allows, students can make their own situations and write the rule as an algebraic expression.

ELL English Language Learners

Rephrase Be sure students understand that *increasing* means getting bigger and bigger, while *decreasing* means getting smaller and smaller.

Additional Resource

Student Math Handbook page 86

Resource Masters

Quiz

Choose the correct answer.

1. What multiplication combination is shown by this array?

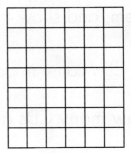

   A. $6 \times 6 = 36$ **C.** $7 \times 7 = 49$

   B. $6 \times 7 = 42$ **D.** $5 \times 7 = 35$

2. What multiplication combination can you find using these 2 arrays?

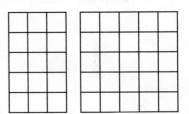

   A. $5 \times 8 = 40$ **C.** $4 \times 7 = 28$

   B. $5 \times 7 = 35$ **D.** $6 \times 7 = 42$

3. What are all of the factors of 28?

   A. 1, 2, 4, 7, 14, 28   **C.** 1, 2, 3, 7, 14, 21, 28

   B. 2, 4, 7, 14   **D.** 1, 2, 4, 7, 28

4. Which number is prime?

   A. 4   **B.** 6   **C.** 13   **D.** 15

5. How can you use 3×9 to find 9×9?

Factors, Multiples, and Arrays

Use What You Know

Solve these story problems. Write a multiplication equation for each problem, and show how you solved the problem.

Blank CDs come in packages of 6.

1. How many CDs are there in 3 packages? _____

    Equation: _____

2. How many CDs are there in 6 packages? _____

    Equation: _____

3. How many CDs are there in 9 packages? _____

    Equation: _____

Constructing Arrays

Solve each problem. Draw the arrays on Centimeter Grid Paper and write the equations below.

1. An artist has 48 paintbrushes. She is drilling holes in a piece of wood to hold the brushes. She wants more than 3 rows of brushes but fewer than 12 rows. Show all the different arrays she can use for her paintbrushes.

2. An artist wants to make a case that holds 72 tubes of paint. He wants at least 4 rows of tubes. He does not want to have more than 10 rows. How many different arrays can he have for his case?

Quiz

Choose the correct answer.

1. $6 \times 8 =$

    A. 24   **B.** 48   **C.** 56   **D.** 68

2. Which number is a factor of 63?

    A. 12   **B.** 11   **C.** 7   **D.** 5

3. Which number is **not** a multiple of 4?

    A. 14   **B.** 16   **C.** 24   **D.** 60

4. $11 \times 7 =$

    A. 117   **B.** 77   **C.** 70   **D.** 63

5. Find a number that is a factor of both 21 and 18.
Explain how you found it.

Factors, Multiples, and Arrays

Missing Numbers

Fill in the chart with the missing factors or products.

Factor	×	Factor	=	Product
6	×		=	54
	×	8	=	96
10	×	11	=	
7	×		=	56
	×	12	=	60
	×	6	=	72
12	×	12	=	
9	×	10	=	
	×	6	=	66

Advanced Multiple Turn Over

For each problem, explain how you know your card is or is not a multiple of the number called.

1. Your partner calls 8. Your card is 52.

2. Your partner calls 4. Your card is 112.

3. Your partner calls 14. Your card is 86.

4. Your partner calls 18. Your card is 108.

5. Your partner calls 17. Your card is 102.

Name   Date

Quiz

Choose the correct answer.

1. Which number is a factor of 100?

    A. 75   **C.** 30

    B. 50   **D.** 15

2. Which number is **not** a factor of 48?

    A. 3   **B.** 4   **C.** 8   **D.** 9

3. Which number is a factor of 36 but **not** a factor of 24?

    A. 2   **C.** 6

    B. 4   **D.** 9

4. Which number times 25 equals 300?

    A. 20   **C.** 12

    B. 18   **D.** 8

5. You know that 1, 2, 4, 5, and 10 are some of the factors of 100. How can that help you find factors of 300?

Factor Pairs and Factors

1. Find all of the factor pairs for 400.

2. List all of the factors of 400. Explain how you know you have found them all.

_____

_____

3. Find all of the factor pairs for 500.

4. List all of the factors of 500. Explain how you know you have found them all.

_____

_____

Use anytime after Session 3.2.

Factor Relationships

Decide whether each statement is true or false. Write *T* or *F* and explain how you know for each one.

1. 10 is a factor of all multiples of 100.   _____

2. Every factor of 100 is a factor of 300.   _____

3. 40 is a factor of any multiple of 100.   _____

4. All factors of 200 are also factors of 300.   _____

Explain how you find the answer.

5. Three factors of 200 are not factors of 100. What are they?

Quiz

Use the line plot to choose the correct answer.

**Number of Bags People Have
When Leaving a Grocery Store**

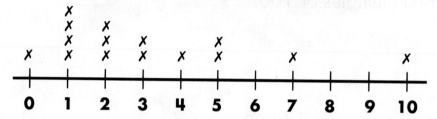

1. What are the fewest bags anyone had?

A. 6   **B.** 4   **C.** 1   **D.** 0

2. What is the range of this set of data?

A. 5   **B.** 7   **C.** 9   **D.** 10

3. What is the median?

A. 5   **B.** 3   **C.** 2   **D.** 1

4. Which might be considered an outlier on this line plot?

A. no outlier   **B.** 0   **C.** 5   **D.** 10

5. What is the typical number of bags people had coming out of the grocery store? How do the data support your thinking?

Describing Data

20 people each took a handful of walnuts.
The line plot shows the data.

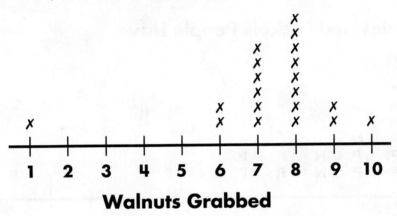

Walnuts Grabbed

1. What seems to be the typical number of walnuts?
Explain why you think so.

_____

_____

_____

2. Are there any outliers? If so, what is it and what might
account for this unusual piece of data?

_____

_____

_____

Statements About Data

20 people were asked how many pennies and nickels they had with them. The line plot shows the data.

Pennies and Nickels People Have

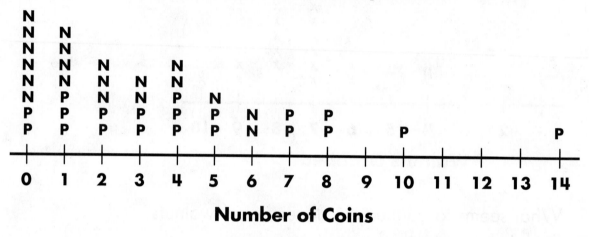

Number of Coins

1. Write 3 statements about the number of pennies and nickels people had with them.

2. What is the typical number of pennies people had with them? Why would you say this is typical?

3. What is the typical number of nickels people had with them? Why would you say this is typical?

Quiz

Use these line plots to choose the correct answer.

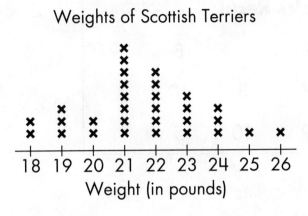

Weights of Scottish Terriers

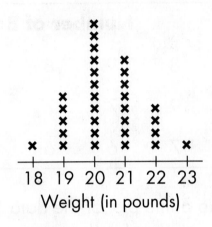

Weights of Beagles

1. What is the range of the weights of the Scottish terriers?

A. 5 pounds   **B.** 7 pounds   **C.** 8 pounds   **D.** 10 pounds

2. What is the median weight of the beagles?

A. 21 pounds   **B.** 20 pounds   **C.** 11 pounds   **D.** 8 pounds

3. Which graph or graphs have outliers?

A. neither   **C.** both

B. beagles only   **D.** Scottish terriers only

4. What is the weight of the heaviest dog?

A. 11 pounds   **B.** 20 pounds   **C.** 21 pounds   **D.** 26 pounds

5. How do the weights of the 2 groups compare?

The Shape of Data

Yuki took a survey of his class about the number of books read last month. The table shows the data.

Number of Books Read							
10	8	9	8	7	9	8	9
14	9	7	7	7	8	10	
7	7	6	6	9	10	5	

1. Make a line plot of the data Yuki collected. Remember to label your line plot.

2. What is the range? How did you find it?

3. What is the median? How did you find it?

4. Write 3 statements that describe the data.

Data Characteristics

Jill recorded the number of people who came to dance class each week.

Number of People at Dance Class						
16	20	18	12	17	16	19
21	16	17	19	18	18	20
14	21	17	18	17	19	

1. Represent the data in a line plot or bar graph.

2. Describe the data. Include the range of the data, how it clumps or spreads out, what the median is, and what is typical.

_____

_____

_____

_____

_____

Quiz

Choose the correct answer.

1. Which event is impossible?

  A. a dog walking on 2 legs   **C.** a cat napping in a car

  B. a house growing wings   **D.** a bird flying at night

2. If you toss a coin, what is the probability of getting a head?

  A. 0   **B.** $\frac{1}{2}$ **C.** 1   **D.** 2

3. You toss a cube numbered from 1 to 6. Which describes the probability of getting a number greater than 2?

  A. more than $\frac{1}{2}$ **C.** less than $\frac{1}{2}$

  B. $\frac{1}{2}$ **D.** 0

4. You grab a cube out of a bag with 8 blue cubes and 2 red cubes. Which describes the likelihood of grabbing a blue cube?

  A. impossible   **B.** unlikely   **C.** likely   **D.** certain

5. There are 3 red cubes and 2 blue cubes in a bag. In an experiment of 50 trials, predict the number of times you would draw a red cube from the bag. Explain your reasoning.

Comparing Experiments

Do another 50 trials of the experiments you did in class.
Add your results to the class line plot.

Experiment 2: 5 red cubes and 15 blue cubes

1. How many red cubes did you draw in 50 trials? _____

2. Did the number you got surprise you, or is it about what you expected? Why?

_____

_____

Experiment 3: 15 red cubes and 5 blue cubes

3. How many red cubes did you draw in 50 trials? _____

4. Did the number you got surprise you, or is it about what you expected? Why?

_____

_____

5. What do you notice when you compare the results from the 2 experiments?

_____

_____

Predictions

Do 50 trials of this experiment:

Experiment 1: 15 red cubes and 10 blue cubes

1. How many red cubes do you predict you will draw

in 50 trials? _____

How many blue cubes? _____

2. How many red cubes did you draw in 50 trials? _____

How many blue cubes? _____

3. Did the number you got surprise you or is it about
what you expected? Why?

_____

_____

4. Make a line plot of your data. Write 3 statements
about what you notice.

Use anytime after Session 3.3.

Quiz

Choose the correct answer.

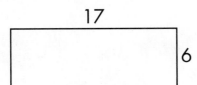

1. How many wheels are on 16 tricycles?

    A. 15   **B.** 24   **C.** 36   **D.** 48

2. Find the product. $13 \times 6 =$

    A. 96   **B.** 78   **C.** 64   **D.** 58

3. Which expression can you use to find 15×4?

    A. $(10 \times 4) + (5 \times 4)$ **C.** $(8 \times 4) + (5 \times 4)$

    B. $(10 \times 2) + (5 \times 2)$ **D.** $(8 \times 8) + (7 \times 8)$

4. There are 4 candles in a box. How many
candles are in 14 boxes?

    A. 28   **B.** 42   **C.** 46   **D.** 56

5. Find the product for 17×6 using combinations
you know. Use equations to show your thinking.

17

6

Arrays and Equations

Solve these problems. Show your thinking.

1. How many sails are on 15 sailboats?

2. How many balloons are in 26 bunches?

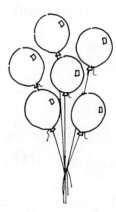

3. 4 × 13 =

4. 22 × 5 =

Use anytime after Session 1.4.

Breaking Apart Numbers

Solve these story problems. Show your thinking.

1. Mrs. Thompson bought 8 boxes of crayons for her class. Each box contains 32 crayons. How many crayons did she buy?

2. The Math Club bought 29 packages of hot dogs for a group picnic. Hot dogs come in packages of 8. How many hot dogs did they buy?

3. Noemi bought 9 boxes of dog biscuits. The dog biscuits come in boxes of 36. How many dog biscuits did she buy?

Quiz

Choose the correct answer.

1. The 48 members of the track team are divided into groups of 3. How many groups are there?

    A. 144   **B.** 14   **C.** 16   **D.** 18

2. $72 \div 4 =$

    A. 9   **B.** 12   **C.** 16   **D.** 18

3. What is the missing factor?

    $7 \times \underline{\hspace{2cm}} = 56$

    A. 392   **B.** 16   **C.** 8   **D.** 6

4. A group of 47 people is having lunch. A table seats 4 people. How many tables are needed for the group?

    A. 11   **B.** 11 R3   **C.** $11\frac{3}{4}$ **D.** 12

5. Write a story for this division problem. Then solve it.

    $65 \div 5$

Division Stories

Solve each problem. Show your work. Write an equation for each one.

1. Mr. Soto set up 84 chairs for a meeting. There are 7 chairs in each row. How many rows of chairs are there?

2. Ms. Santiago had 90 packages of candles. The candles come in packages of 6. How many packages of candles does she have?

3. A student made $112 washing cars. He charged $8 for each car. How many cars did he wash?

Making Sense of Remainders

Solve these problems. Show your work.

1. Jill bought a bag of 50 beads to make key
chains. She uses 6 beads for each key chain.
How many key chains can she make?

Answer: _____ key chains

2. Mr. Blake is packing 79 books into boxes.
He can pack 12 books in each box.
How many boxes does he need?

Answer: _____ boxes

3. Mrs. Sanchez is ordering vans for a class field trip.
There are 45 students in the class. Each van can
hold 6 students. How many vans does she need?

Answer: _____ vans

Use anytime after Session 2.4.

Quiz

Choose the correct answer.

1. $6 \times 10 =$

    A. 6   **B.** 60   **C.** 66   **D.** 600

2. $30 \times 7 =$

    A. 2,100   **B.** 370   **C.** 210   **D.** 37

3. $15 \times 20 =$

    A. 30   **B.** 300   **C.** 152   **D.** 3,000

4. $4 \times 50 =$

    A. 500   **B.** 300   **C.** 250   **D.** 200

5. Write a story for this multiplication problem.
Then solve it.

    6×40

Multiplication Stories

Solve these problems. Show your solutions with equations.
You may also use arrays or pictures.

1. The owner of a grocery store ordered 30 cartons
of juice. There are 6 bottles of juice in a carton.
How many bottles of juice were ordered?

2. There are 12 packages of popcorn in a box.
A factory received an order for 50 boxes.
How many packages of popcorn are needed
to fill the order?

3. Ms. Karl owns 8 bakeries. She ordered
150 pounds of flour for each bakery. How many
pounds of flour did she order?

Use anytime after Session 3.3.

About Multiples

Answer the questions about this multiplication tower.

1. What number was used to build the tower?

_____

2. How many multiples are in the tower? _____

3. What is one way to figure out how many multiples are in the tower without counting each one?

4. Write an equation for the 25th multiple and explain how you got your answer.

5. Write an equation for the 32nd multiple and explain how your got your answer.

1,800
1,710
1,620
1,530
1,440
1,350
1,260
1,170
1,080
990
900
810
720
630
540
450
360
270
180
90

Quiz

Choose the correct answer.

1. $20 \times 16 =$

   A. 32   **B.** 36   **C.** 320   **D.** 360

2. There are 6 muffins in a box. How many muffins are in 14 boxes?

   A. 624   **B.** 200   **C.** 84   **D.** 64

3. $32 \times 4 =$

   A. 64   **B.** 128   **C.** 158   **D.** 200

4. A foot is 12 inches. How many inches are in 25 feet?

   A. 400   **B.** 300   **C.** 256   **D.** 84

5. Find the product for 15×8. Use equations to show your thinking.

Multiplication Strategies

Solve these problems. Show your solutions with equations.

1. $17 \times 4 =$

2. $22 \times 6 =$

3. $40 \times 15 =$

4. $36 \times 4 =$

5. $19 \times 12 =$

6. Choose one of the problems above and solve it
a second way, using a different strategy than the
one you used the first time.

Pairs of Problems

1. Solve the first problem in each pair. Can you use the
first problem to help you solve the second problem?

a. $10 \times 7 =$ _____   **b.** $8 \times 8 =$ _____

$5 \times 14 =$ _____ $16 \times 8 =$ _____

c. $12 \times 8 =$ _____   **d.** $8 \times 9 =$ _____

$24 \times 4 =$ _____ $8 \times 18 =$ _____

e. $12 \times 10 =$ _____   **f.** $6 \times 7 =$ _____

$4 \times 30 =$ _____ $6 \times 14 =$ _____

2. Choose one pair of equations from **1b**, **1d**, or **1f**.

a. Use arrays, pictures, cubes, or a story
context to show both problems in the pair.

b. What is different about each problem in this
pair? What is the same? How does the first
problem help you solve the second problem?

Use anytime after Session 4.1.

Name	Date	

Size, Shape, and Symmetry

Quiz

Choose the correct answer.

1. Which unit of measurement is the longest?

    A. 1 foot   **B.** 1 meter   **C.** 1 inch   **D.** 1 centimeter

2. Which of these is about 1 yard long?

    A. school bus   **B.** computer   **C.** baseball bat   **D.** classroom

3. What is the perimeter of this rectangle?

    A. 12 cm

    B. 16 cm

    C. 20 cm

    D. 32 cm

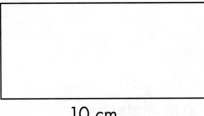

4. The perimeter is 37 inches. How long is the missing side?

    A. 10 inches

    B. 12 inches

    C. 27 inches

    D. 47 inches

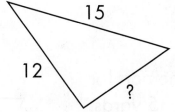

5. Alejandro measured the perimeter of a table and got 18 feet. Cheyenne measured the same table and got 15 feet. Write at least 2 reasons why their measurements are different.

Perimeters of Shapes

Imagine that each shape below is a part of a flower garden. For each shape, find the missing measure to complete the perimeter.

1. The perimeter of the part for the roses is 190 feet. The missing measure

is _____ feet.

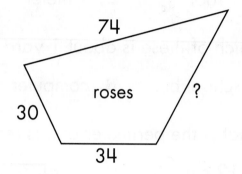

2. The perimeter of the part for the tulips is 248 meters. The missing measure is

_____ meters.

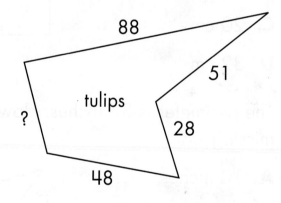

3. The perimeter of the part for the sunflowers is 235 yards. The missing measure is

_____ yards.

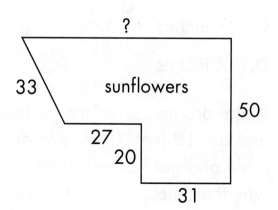

Use anytime after Session 1.5.

Finding Perimeters

1. Estimate and then find the perimeters of the objects listed below.

Object	Estimate	Perimeter
The floor of your classroom		
A wall of your classroom		
A hallway in your school		
Your room at home		

2. Use masking tape to make 2 different paths with the same perimeter. Each path must start and end at the same place. Draw your paths below. How are they different?

Quiz

Use the diagram at the right. Choose the correct answer.

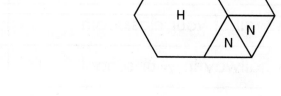

1. This polygon is made with 5 shapes.
What is its name?

   A. triangle

   B. pentagon

   C. quadrilateral

   D. hexagon

2. Which shapes in the polygon are quadrilaterals?

   A. only K   **C.** K and M

   B. only M   **D.** K, M, and N

3. Which 2 shapes make a pentagon?

   A. H and N   **C.** M and N

   B. H and K   **D.** K and M

4. The 2 N shapes make a polygon.
How many sides does it have?

   A. 3   **B.** 4   **C.** 5   **D.** 6

5. Use 2 squares to make a rectangle.
How is the rectangle like each square?
How is it different?

Naming Polygons

Count the number of sides in each new polygon made from Power Polygon shapes. Write the name of each new polygon. Is it a triangle, a quadrilateral, a pentagon, a hexagon, or an octagon?

1.

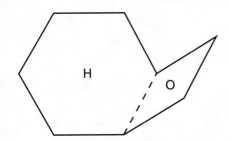

Name of Polygon:

_____

2.

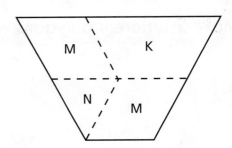

Name of Polygon:

_____

3.

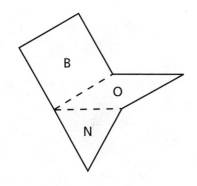

Name of Polygon:

_____

4.

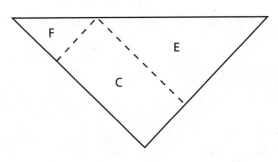

Name of Polygon:

_____

Making New Polygons

Start with the hexagon from the Power Polygon set. Add one more shape. Trace each new polygon. Draw dashed lines to show the sides of the Power Polygons that you used. Then write the letter inside of each shape.

1. Make 2 different polygons with 8 sides.

2. Make 1 polygon with fewer than 8 sides.
   Make 1 with more than 8 sides.

Quiz

Choose the correct answer.

1. Which shape has a right angle?

A.   **B.**   **C.**   **D.**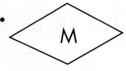

2. Which shape has an angle greater than 90 degrees?

A.   **B.**   **C.**    **D.**

3. Which shape does **not** have 2 acute angles?

A.   **B.** 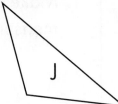   **C.** 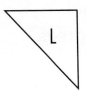   **D.**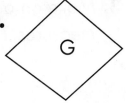

4. An angle is half as big as a right angle. How many degrees does it have?

   A. 30   **B.** 45   **C.** 60   **D.** 180

5. Explain how to use the angles in triangle N to find the angle measures in shapes M and G.

Building Acute and Obtuse Angles

Use the angles of 2 or more Power Polygons to make the angles described. Trace the polygons that you used and label them with their letters.

1. Make an angle that measures 60 degrees.

2. Make an angle that measures 90 degrees.

3. Make an angle that measures 120 degrees.

4. Make an angle that measures 150 degrees.

Finding Equal Angles

Use Power Polygons to answer each question.

1. The squares have 4 right angles. Write the degrees in one of these angles.

_____ degrees

Find all the other shapes that have this angle.

_____

2. Shape N has 3 angles. Each angle is the same size. Write the degrees in one of these angles.

_____ degrees

Find all the other shapes that have this angle.

_____

3. Shape E has 2 angles that are less than 90 degrees. Write the degrees in one of these angles.

_____ degrees

Find all the other shapes that have this angle.

_____

4. Shape J has 2 angles that are less than 90 degrees. Write the degrees in one of these angles.

_____ degrees

Find all the other shapes that have one of these angles.

_____

Quiz

Choose the correct answer.

1. How many gray triangles cover the area of the polygon?

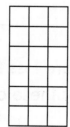

A. 3   **C.** 6

B. 4   **D.** 7

2. How many square units are there in the area of the trapezoid?

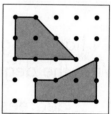

A. 5   **C.** 3

B. 4   **D.** 2

3. How many square units are there in the area of the pentagon?

A. 4   **C.** 6

B. 5   **D.** 8

4. Which rectangle has the greatest area?

A. 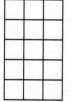   **B.**   **C.**   **D.**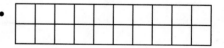

5. Build a shape on the Geoboard. Join a triangle to a rectangle to make the shape. Find the area of your shape.

Find the Area

Find the area of each shape and explain how you found your answer.

1.

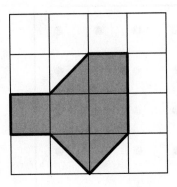

2.

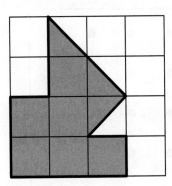

3.

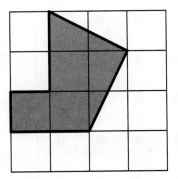

4.

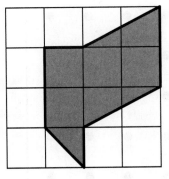

Polygon Areas

Build each shape on your Geoboard. Find the area.

1. right triangle

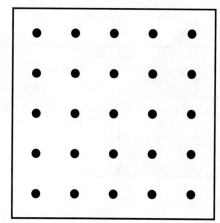

Area: _____

2. trapezoid

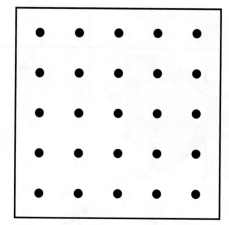

Area: _____

3. pentagon

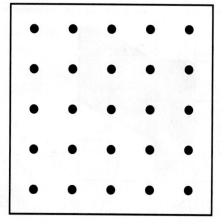

Area: _____

4. hexagon

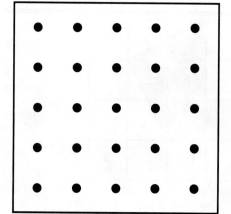

Area: _____

Quiz

Choose the correct answer.

1. Which numeral is three hundred eighteen?

   A. 308   **B.** 318   **C.** 380   **D.** 381

2. What is 200 less than 765?

   A. 965   **B.** 745   **C.** 565   **D.** 543

3. What is 40 more than 567?

   A. 527   **B.** 571   **C.** 607   **D.** 967

4. How many 10s are there in 360?

   A. 63   **B.** 36   **C.** 6   **D.** 3

5. You plan to travel 1,000 miles. So far, you have
   gone 485 miles. Explain how to find the number
   of miles you still need to go.

Adding and Subtracting 1s, 10s, and 100s

Complete these equations. Use your 1,000 book to help.

1. Count by 100s. How many 100s do you need to get to each number?

300   600   1,000   400

_____   _____   _____   _____

2. Count by 10s. How many 10s do you need to get to each number?

200   410   780   550

_____   _____   _____   _____

3. $432 + 1 =$ _____

$432 - 1 =$ _____

$432 + 10 =$ _____

$432 - 10 =$ _____

4. $972 + 1 =$ _____

$972 - 1 =$ _____

$972 + 10 =$ _____

$972 - 10 =$ _____

5. $659 + 1 =$ _____

$659 - 1 =$ _____

$659 + 100 =$ _____

$659 - 100 =$ _____

6. $294 + 1 =$ _____

$294 - 1 =$ _____

$294 + 100 =$ _____

$294 - 100 =$ _____

Use anytime after Session 1.3.

Using the 1,000 Book

Write each number in your 1,000 book. Then write
the chart on which the number belongs. Use the last
number on a chart to name it.

1. 375 is on the _____ chart.　　**2.** 962 is on the _____ chart.

3. 71 is on the _____ chart.　　**4.** 522 is on the _____ chart.

5. 804 is on the _____ chart.　　**6.** 298 is on the _____ chart.

Choose 2 numbers on each chart. Tell how to find
the difference between your 2 numbers.

7. _____ and _____ are on the 700 chart.

I found the difference by _____

_____

_____

8. _____ and _____ are on the 400 chart.

I found the difference by _____

_____

_____

Quiz

Choose the correct answer.

1. $596 + 208 =$

   A. 624   **B.** 704   **C.** 794   **D.** 804

2.   722
       $+ 538$

   A. 1,360   **B.** 1,350   **C.** 1,260   **D.** 1,250

3. Your family drove 358 miles on Friday and 471 miles on Saturday. How many miles did your family drive altogether?

   A. 729   **B.** 739   **C.** 829   **D.** 839

4. A student spent $4.85 on notebooks and $2.87 on markers. How much did this student spend in all?

   A. $7.72   **B.** $6.72   **C.** $6.62   **D.** $6.02

5. Solve the problem $873 + 796$ by starting with $800 + 700$. Then solve $873 + 796$ another way. Show each solution with clear and concise notation.

Reviewing Addition

1. Draw a sticker model for 39 + 56.
Then add these numbers, and use equations
to show your thinking. Show your work.

Solve the following problems.
Show your work, including equations.

2. 48 + 74 =

3. 125 + 57 =

4. 278 + 36 =

Name Date

More Than One Strategy

Solve the following addition problems and show your solutions.
Use 2 different addition strategies.

1. 342 + 576 = ______

2.
```
  197
+ 548
-----
```

For each problem, choose 2 things from the chart to buy.
Use 2 different addition strategies to find the total prices.

Book	Game	Movie	Toy Car	Plant
$3.87	$11.75	$6.98	$14.49	$8.50

3. I'll buy a ______ and a ______.

The total price will be ______ + ______.

4. I'll buy a ______ and a ______.

The total price will be ______ + ______.

Use anytime after Session 2.2.

Quiz

Choose the correct answer.

1. Which number is between 5,001 and 6,000?

    A. 4,965   **B.** 5,960   **C.** 6,050   **D.** 6,500

2. 5,263 − 2,000 + 80 =

    A. 3,343   **B.** 3,240   **C.** 3,220   **D.** 3,214

3. What places change when you add 500 to 3,621?

    A. hundreds   **C.** tens and hundreds

    B. thousands   **D.** hundreds and thousands

4. 3,086 + 937 =

    A. 4,023   **B.** 4,013   **C.** 3,923   **D.** 3,913

5. How many 10s are in 1,847? Explain how you figured it out.

Landmarks and Large Numbers

What Places Change?

Solve each problem, showing your solutions clearly. Write which place value(s) in the first number changed.

1. 5,063 + 400 − 30 = _____

Place value(s) that changed: _____

2. 7,827 − 3,000 + 40 = _____

Place value(s) that changed: _____

3. 2,849 + 600 − 1,000 = _____

Place value(s) that changed: _____

4. 5,505 − 80 + 800 = _____

Place value(s) that changed: _____

Use anytime after Session 3.4.

More Road Trips

Use the driving distance table on page 46 of the *Student Activity Book*. Write where you start, end, and the cities you visit. Find the total miles. Show your solution on the back of this sheet.

1. Use 3 cities. Plan a trip close to 3,000 miles.

Cities: _____

Total Miles: _____

2. Use 3 cities. Plan a trip between 3,000 and 4,000 miles.

Cities: _____

Total Miles: _____

3. Use 4 cities. Plan a trip shorter than 4,000 miles.

Cities: _____

Total Miles: _____

4. Use 5 cities. Plan a trip close to 5,000 miles.

Cities: _____

Total Miles: _____

Quiz

Choose the correct answer.

1. 473 − 217 =

A. 156   **B.** 256   **C.** 264   **D.** 266

2.   509
   − 182

A. 473   **B.** 427   **C.** 417   **D.** 327

3. Eastlake School has 684 boys and 715 girls. How many more girls than boys are there at the school?

A. 31   **B.** 169   **C.** 171   **D.** 1,399

4. You are traveling to visit a friend. She lives 815 miles away. You traveled 357 miles the first day. How many miles do you still have to travel?

A. 568   **B.** 542   **C.** 462   **D.** 458

5. Solve the problem 646 − 298 in 2 different ways. Show your work clearly.

Choosing Starter Problems

Subtract. Write your starter problem and show your strategy.

1. 128 − 76 = _____   Starter Problem: _____

My strategy:

2. 349 − 126 = _____   Starter Problem: _____

My strategy:

3. 782 − 349 = _____   Starter Problem: _____

My strategy:

4. 808 − 491 = _____   Starter Problem: _____

My strategy:

Change and Adjust

Solve each subtraction problem by changing one number and adjusting or by changing both numbers to make an equivalent problem. Show your strategy.

1. $276 - 149 = $ _____

2. $365 - 187 = $ _____

3. $1,146 - 728 = $ _____

4. $4,389 - 1,675 = $ _____

5. Does changing one number or making an equivalent problem always make the problem easier to solve? Why do you think so?

Quiz

Choose the correct answer.

1. What fraction of this rectangle is shaded?

    A. $\frac{5}{3}$ **C.** $\frac{3}{5}$

    B. $\frac{5}{8}$ **D.** $\frac{3}{8}$

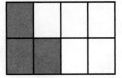

2. What is $\frac{1}{4}$ of 24?

    A. 3   **B.** 4   **C.** 6   **D.** 8

3. There are 60 fourth graders at Jefferson School. One fifth of them are in the school choir. How many are in the choir?

    A. 15   **B.** 12   **C.** 10   **D.** 6

4. What fraction is equal to $\frac{1}{3}$?

    A. $\frac{2}{6}$ **B.** $\frac{3}{6}$ **C.** $\frac{4}{6}$ **D.** $\frac{5}{6}$

5. Solve the problem and show your solution.

Three people shared a bag of 24 oranges. One person took $\frac{1}{8}$ of the oranges, and one person took $\frac{1}{2}$ of the oranges. How many oranges are left for the third person?

Fractional Parts of a Rectangle

Use these rectangles to show the following fractions as clearly as you can. Explain your thinking about each one.

1. $\frac{3}{8}$

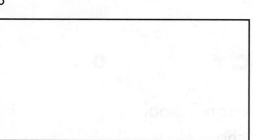

2. $\frac{4}{4}$

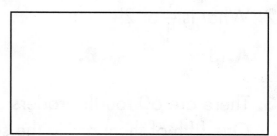

3. $\frac{3}{6}$

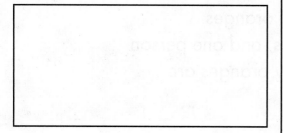

4. $\frac{1}{3}$

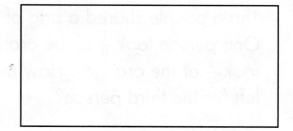

Use anytime after Session 1.5.

Fraction Cards and Decimal Squares

How Many?

Solve each problem and show your solution.

1. In an art class, $\frac{3}{5}$ of the 25 students are painting landscapes. The rest are painting portraits. How many students are painting portraits?

2. Of the 30 students in a cooking class, $\frac{3}{10}$ are baking muffins. How many students are baking muffins?

3. There are 48 people in a gymnastics class. This is the first class $\frac{5}{12}$ of the people have taken. How many people are taking the gymnastics class for the first time?

Quiz

Choose the correct answer.

1. Which fraction is greater than 1?

A. $\frac{8}{8}$ **B.** $\frac{1}{6}$ **C.** $\frac{0}{2}$ **D.** $\frac{4}{3}$

2. Which fraction is equal to $\frac{1}{2}$?

A. $\frac{4}{4}$ **B.** $\frac{4}{6}$ **C.** $\frac{3}{6}$ **D.** $\frac{3}{8}$

3. Which shows the fractions in order from least to greatest?

A. $\frac{1}{2}, \frac{1}{3}, \frac{5}{6}$ **C.** $\frac{1}{3}, \frac{5}{6}, \frac{1}{2}$

B. $\frac{1}{3}, \frac{1}{2}, \frac{5}{6}$ **D.** $\frac{5}{6}, \frac{1}{2}, \frac{1}{3}$

4. Which number sentence is true?

A. $\frac{1}{3} + \frac{2}{3} = 1$ **C.** $\frac{1}{4} + \frac{1}{2} = 1$

B. $\frac{1}{4} + \frac{1}{2} > 1$ **D.** $\frac{1}{3} + \frac{2}{3} < 1$

5. Fill in the blank to make the equation true.
Tell how you found the answer.

$\frac{3}{8} + \frac{1}{4} + \underline{\hspace{1.5cm}} = 1$

Fix the Order

The fractions on each line are out of order. Use an arrow to show how to fix the order with just one move.

1. $\dfrac{1}{2}$ $\dfrac{1}{3}$ $\dfrac{3}{5}$ $\dfrac{2}{3}$ $\dfrac{3}{2}$

2. $\dfrac{1}{5}$ $\dfrac{1}{4}$ $\dfrac{2}{5}$ $\dfrac{3}{4}$ $\dfrac{3}{5}$

3. $\dfrac{2}{12}$ $\dfrac{1}{3}$ $\dfrac{3}{12}$ $\dfrac{2}{3}$ $\dfrac{3}{3}$

4. $\dfrac{3}{8}$ $\dfrac{1}{2}$ $\dfrac{5}{8}$ $\dfrac{7}{8}$ $\dfrac{3}{4}$

5. $\dfrac{7}{8}$ $\dfrac{5}{4}$ $1\dfrac{1}{3}$ $1\dfrac{3}{4}$ $\dfrac{9}{6}$

Challenging Fractions

Use the landmarks 0, $\frac{1}{2}$, 1, and 2 to help you place each of the following fractions on the number line. Write each fraction in its place.

1. $\frac{5}{12}$

2. $\frac{9}{5}$

3. $\frac{11}{5}$

4. $\frac{15}{12}$

5. $\frac{7}{15}$

6. $\frac{5}{9}$

7. $\frac{1}{10}$

8. $\frac{8}{9}$

9. $\frac{5}{7}$

0    $\frac{1}{2}$ 1   2

Use anytime after Session 2.5.

Name

Date

Fraction Cards and Decimal Squares

Quiz

Choose the correct answer.

1. What part of the grid is shaded?

   A. 0.37

   B. 0.53

   C. 0.63

   D. 6.3

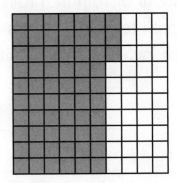

2. Which number is greater than 0.5?

   A. 0.05   **B.** 0.75   **C.** 0.45   **D.** 0.50

3. Which number is 6 tenths?

   A. 6.0   **B.** 0.66   **C.** 0.6   **D.** 0.06

4. 0.03 + 1.22 =

   A. 1.25   **B.** 1.52   **C.** 1.55   **D.** 4.22

5. Write a decimal on each of the 2 blank cards so that the sum of the 3 cards is 2.0. Tell how you chose each decimal.

Adding Decimal Numbers

Make an imaginary rainfall log. Write a decimal for the
amount of rain that falls each week. Make sure the total
rainfall for the 7 weeks is 13.5 inches. Each rainfall amount
must include tenths or hundredths.

Week	Rainfall (Inches)
1	
2	
3	
4	
5	
6	
7	

How did you make the number of inches add up to 13.5?
How did you think about this problem?

Comparing Tenths and Hundredths

Circle the decimal that is larger. Explain how you
figured out which is more. Then determine how much
greater the decimal is.

1. 0.7   or   0.75

2. 0.30   or   0.03

3. 0.8   or   0.80

4. 0.25   or   0.35

5. 0.9   or   0.65

Quiz

Choose the correct answer.

1. Which solid has a silhouette that is a square?

A. 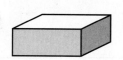 **B.**   **C.**   **D.**

2. Which solid does **not** have a rectangle for a silhouette?

A.   **B.**   **C.**   **D.**

3. Which of these could be a silhouette for a sphere?

A.  **B.**  **C.**  **D.**

4. Which of these could **not** be a silhouette for a prism?

A.  **B.**  **C.**  **D.**

5. Choose 2 different geometric solids that can make the same silhouette. Sketch the solids and the silhouette.

Moving Between Solids and Silhouettes

City Street

Build this city street with your solids. Look at each pair
of silhouettes. Find all the points on the street where
you could stand and see the 2 silhouettes.

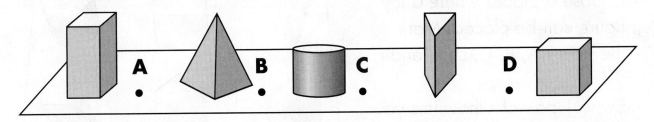

Pair 1

Points from which these could be seen:

_____

Pair 2

Points from which these could be seen:

_____

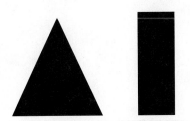

Pair 3

Points from which these could be seen:

_____

Landscape 4

Build this landscape with your
geometric solids.

Choose 6 places where a toy
figure can be placed. Mark
the points A, B, C, D, E, and F.

Draw 1 pair of silhouettes you
can see from each point.

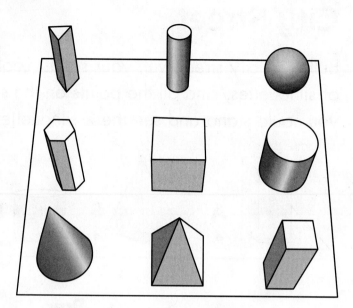

Point A	Point B	Point C
Point D	**Point E**	**Point F**

Moving Between Solids and Silhouettes

Quiz

Choose the correct answer.

1. How many cubes are used to make this cube building?
Top

   A. 6   **C.** 9

   B. 8   **D.** 13

2. Which view shows the top of the building in Problem 1?

   A.   **B.**   **C.**   **D.**

3. How many cubes are used to make this cube building?

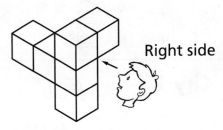

Right side

   A. 9   **C.** 6

   B. 8   **D.** 5

4. Which view shows the right side of the building in Problem 3?

   A.   **B.**   **C.**   **D.**

5. Choose 1 of the cube buildings on this page. Draw the front, top, and right-side views.

More City Views

In each map, the number on top of a building tells how many cubes high that building is. Write the letter that shows the silhouette from that point of view.

City 1

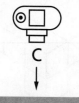

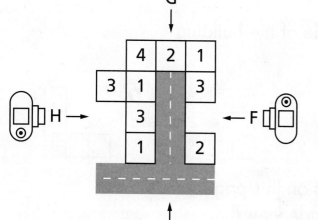

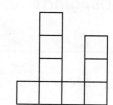 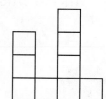

1. _____ 2. _____

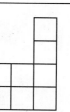 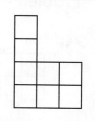

3. _____ 4. _____

City 2

 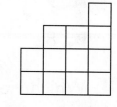

5. _____ 6. _____

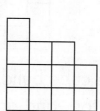 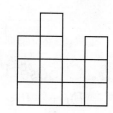

7. _____ 8. _____

Use anytime after Session 2.5.

Six Views of Cube Buildings

On a sheet of grid paper, draw 6 silhouette views
for each cube building. Show the front, back, top,
bottom, right side, and left side.

1.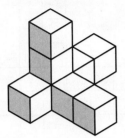

2.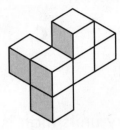

3.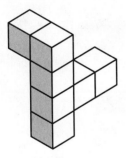

4.

5.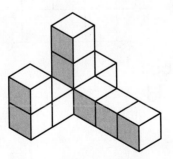

6.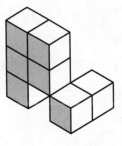

Quiz

Choose the correct answer.

1. What are the dimensions of the bottom layer of Box A?

Box A

A. 2×2 **C.** 3×3

B. 2×3 **D.** 3×8

2. How many units high is Box A?

A. 9   **C.** 3

B. 8   **D.** 2

3. How many cubes fit in a box made from the pattern for Box A above?

A. 12   **C.** 24

B. 18   **D.** 36

4. How many cubes fit in Box B?

Box B

A. 30   **C.** 16

B. 20   **D.** 10

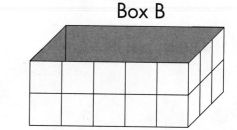

5. Use grid paper to make a pattern for a box. The bottom is 2×5, and the box will hold 30 cubes.

Volume of Boxes

Write the number of unit cubes that fill each box.

1.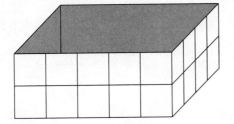

_____

2.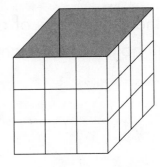

_____

3.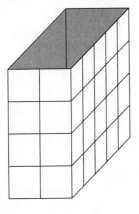

_____

4.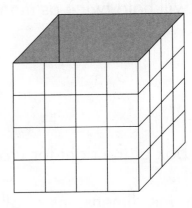

_____

5.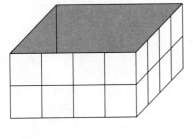

_____

6.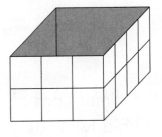

_____

7. Choose 2 boxes on this page. Use grid paper to make a pattern for each box.

Half or Twice as Many

Use the box at the right for Problems 1 and 2.

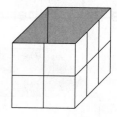

1. Write the dimensions of all the boxes
that will hold half as many cubes.

2. Write the dimensions of all the boxes
that will hold twice as many cubes.

Use the box at the right for Problems 3 and 4.

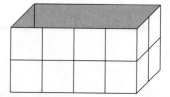

3. Write the dimensions of all the boxes
that will hold half as many cubes.

4. Write the dimensions of all the boxes
that will hold twice as many cubes.

Quiz

Choose the correct answer.

1. $60 \times 5 =$

    A. 30   **B.** 110   **C.** 300   **D.** 400

2. Which is the closest estimate for 35×19?

    A. 800   **B.** 700   **C.** 600   **D.** 350

3. $28 \times 56 =$

    A. 668   **B.** 840   **C.** 1,568   **D.** 2,648

4. There are 32 beads in a package. Ramona bought 21 packages. How many beads did she buy?

    A. 105   **B.** 483   **C.** 630   **D.** 672

5. Write a story to go with 36×52. Then solve it.

Picturing Multiplication Problems

Solve each story problem. Show your solution.
You may include arrays or pictures of groups.

1. There are 24 plants in a tray. Mr. Peters bought
32 trays for the hospital garden. How many plants
did he buy?

2. There are 18 tables in the lunchroom. There are
12 chairs at each table. How many chairs are
there in the lunchroom?

3. There are 36 carrots in a bag. The owner of a
restaurant bought 18 bags of carrots. How many
carrots did she buy?

Cluster Problems

Solve the problems in each cluster. Show your strategy
for solving the final problem. Put a star next to any of
the problems in the cluster that helped you.

1. Solve these problems:

$47 \times 10 =$ _____

$40 \times 6 =$ _____

$7 \times 6 =$ _____

Now solve $47 \times 16 =$

2. Solve these problems:

$4 \times 32 =$ _____

$5 \times 32 =$ _____

$50 \times 32 =$ _____

Now solve $54 \times 32 =$

3. Solve these problems:

$22 \times 2 =$ _____

$22 \times 4 =$ _____

$22 \times 20 =$ _____

Now solve $22 \times 24 =$

Quiz

Choose the correct answer.

1. There are 25 apples in a box. An apple grower sold 22 boxes of apples. How many apples did he sell?

   A. 550   **B.** 500   **C.** 450   **D.** 440

2. Richard is solving 36×75. Which smaller problems can he solve to find the final answer?

   A. 30×6 70×5 6×70 30×5

   B. 30×70 30×5 6×70 6×5

   C. 3×7 3×5 6×3 7×5

   D. 30×70 30×50 60×70 60×50

3. $56 \times 44 =$

   A. 2,032   **B.** 2,224   **C.** 2,464   **D.** 2,860

4. Anna started solving 19×24 by multiplying $20 \times 24 = 480$. What should she do next?

   A. Add 19.   **C.** Subtract 19.

   B. Add 24.   **D.** Subtract 24.

5. Write a story problem for 61×43. Solve it. Show your solution.

Multiplication Stories

Write a story problem for each problem. Then solve
the problem and show your solution.

1. $78 \times 51 =$ _____

   Story problem:

   Solution:

2. $89 \times 38 =$ _____

   Story problem:

   Solution:

3. $19 \times 64 =$ _____

   Story problem:

   Solution:

Multiplying 3-Digit Numbers

Write a story problem for each problem. Then solve
the problem and show your solution.

1. 281 × 36 = _____

Story problem:

Solution:

2. 502 × 62 = _____

Story problem:

Solution:

3. 416 × 25 = _____

Story problem:

Solution:

Quiz

Choose the correct answer.

1. What is a good first step for finding $144 \div 9$?

    A. $9 \times 10 = 90$ **C.** $14 \div 9 = 1\ R5$

    B. $144 \div 10 = 14\ R4$ **D.** $144 \times 9 = 1{,}296$

2. Which equation does **not** show how 16, 12, and 192 are related?

    A. $16 \times 12 = 192$ **C.** $192 \div 12 = 16$

    B. $192 \div 16 = 12$ **D.** $12 \times 192 = 16$

3. How many teams of 16 can 448 students make?

    A. 18   **B.** 22   **C.** 24   **D.** 28

4. $374 \div 12$

    A. 32 R1   **B.** 31 R2   **C.** 30 R14   **D.** 21 R2

5. Write a story problem for the division problem shown below. Solve the problem and show your solution.

$288 \div 24 =$

Stories for Division

Write a story problem to go with each division problem.
Then solve the division problem and show your solution.

1. 252 ÷ 14 =

Story problem:

Solution:

2. 182 ÷ 7 =

Story problem:

Solution:

3. 221 ÷ 13 =

Story problem:

Solution:

Dividing with Larger Numbers

In each story problem about vases, each vase holds
the same number of flowers. Solve each problem
and show your solution. You may include a picture
to show your thinking.

1. There are 450 flowers to go into 18 vases.
How many flowers go in each vase?

2. There are 384 flowers to go into 24 vases.
How many flowers go in each vase?

3. There are 682 flowers to go into 31 vases.
How many flowers go in each vase?

Quiz

Choose the correct answer.
Graph 1 shows a car's speed.
Use Graph 1 in Problems 1–2.

Graph 1

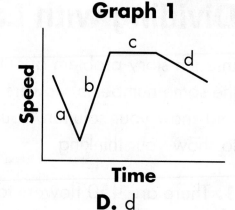

1. When did the speed increase?

A. a   **B.** b   **C.** c   **D.** d

2. When did the speed stay the same?

A. a   **B.** b   **C.** c   **D.** d

Graph 2 shows temperatures.
Use Graph 2 in Problems 3–5.

3. What is the temperature
at 10:00 A.M.?

A. 1°F   **C.** 13°F

B. 5°F   **D.** 20°F

Graph 2

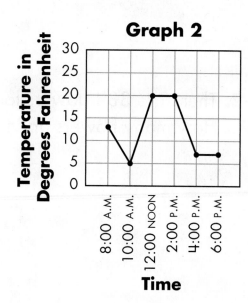

4. What happens to the temperature from
10:00 A.M. to noon?

A. Increases   **C.** Stays the same

B. Decreases   **D.** Equals zero

5. How much warmer was it at 2:00 P.M.
than at 4:00 P.M.? How do you know?

City Temperatures

The table shows city temperatures at the start of each month. Graph the data on the grid below.

Date	Temperature
Oct. 1	42°F
Nov. 1	33°F
Dec. 1	20°F
Jan. 1	12°F
Feb. 1	22°F
Mar. 1	38°F
Apr. 1	53°F
May 1	57°F

1. On which date was it the coldest?

_____

2. On which date was it the warmest?

_____

3. Between which 2 months did the temperature change the least?

_____

4. In which 2 months did the temperature decrease the most?

_____

5. How does the temperature change from Dec. 1 to Feb. 1?

_____

_____

_____

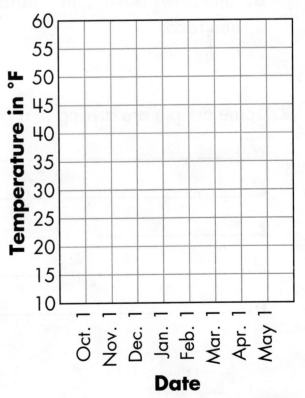

Speed Graphs

Sketch a graph for each situation. Show the changes in speed. Write the letters on the parts of the graphs. For Problem 2, first complete your own story.

1. A runner is in a race.

    a. She starts at 0 and increases to her fastest speed.

    b. She runs at that speed for a while.

    c. She slows down.

    d. She runs at a slower speed for a while.

    e. She slows down and finishes the race.

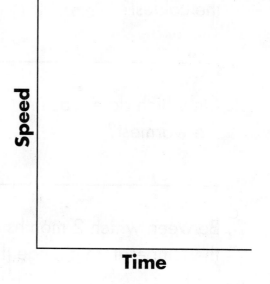

2. Some people are driving in a car.

    a. _____

    b. _____

    c. _____

    d. _____

    e. _____

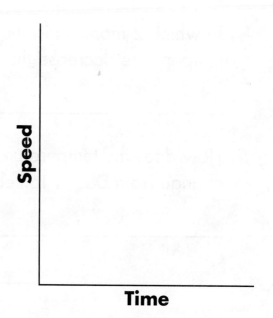

Quiz

Choose the correct answer.

1. Penny Jar A starts with 7 pennies, and 4 pennies are added in each round. How many pennies are there all together after Round 5?

A. 23   **B.** 27   **C.** 28   **D.** 39

2. Penny Jar B starts with 10 pennies, and 2 pennies are added in each round. Jar C starts with 1 penny, and 5 are added in each round. When will Jar C have the same amount of pennies as Jar B?

A. never   **C.** after Round 3

B. after Round 2   **D.** after Round 10

3. There are 8 floors in a single tower made with connecting cubes. How many windows (including the skylight) are there?

A. 33   **C.** 17

B. 32   **D.** 16

Skylight

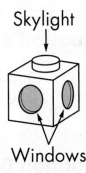

Windows

4. In a double tower, which number of windows (including skylights) is **not** possible?

A. 8   **B.** 20   **C.** 32   **D.** 60

5. A Penny Jar starts with 5 pennies. Then 3 pennies are added in each round. Explain how to find the total number of pennies in any round.

Comparing Penny Jars

Complete each table. Then draw a graph on M29.

1. Situation A:

Start with 4 pennies.
Add 6 each round.

Situation B:

Start with 2 pennies.
Add 6 each round.

Round	Total Number of Pennies	
	Situation A	Situation B
Start		
1		
2		
5		
10		

Will Penny Jar B ever catch up with Penny Jar A? _____

2. Situation A:

Start with 20 pennies.
Add 2 each round.

Situation B:

Start with 3 pennies.
Add 4 each round.

Round	Total Number of Pennies	
	Situation A	Situation B
Start		
1		
2		
5		
10		

Will Penny Jar B ever catch up with Penny Jar A? _____

Use anytime after Session 2.5.

Bigger Penny Jars

Create 2 Penny Jar situations with numbers greater than 20.
Graph your situations on centimeter grid paper.

1. Start with _____.

Add _____ each round.

Number of Rounds	Total Number of Pennies
Start with	
1	
2	
3	
4	
5	
7	
10	
20	
30	

2. Start with _____.

Add _____ each round.

Number of Rounds	Total Number of Pennies
Start with	
1	
2	
3	
4	
5	
7	
10	
20	
30	

Quiz

Choose the correct answer.

1. Graph 1 shows a plant's growth. How tall was it on Wednesday?

A. 3 cm   **C.** 15 cm

B. 13 cm   **D.** 20 cm

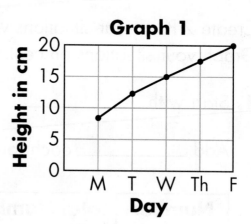

Graph 1

Graph 2 shows another plant's growth.
Use Graph 2 in Problems 2–4.

2. When did the plant stop growing for a while?

A. a   **C.** c

B. b   **D.** d

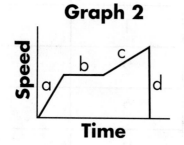

Graph 2

3. When did the plant grow the fastest?

A. a   **C.** c

B. b   **D.** d

4. When was the plant pulled out?

A. a   **C.** c

B. b   **D.** d

5. Draw a graph on the back of this sheet that shows this story: A plant grew very quickly for a while. The top of the plant broke off. Then the plant grew more slowly than at the beginning.

Making Plant Graphs

The tables show the growth of 2 plants.
Make a graph for each table.

Table 1

Day	Height (cm)
Monday	1
Tuesday	1.5
Wednesday	2
Thursday	2.5
Friday	3.5
Saturday	5
Sunday	7

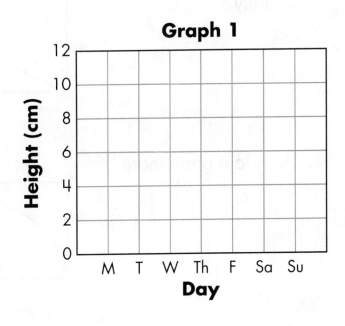

Graph 1

Table 2

Day	Height (cm)
Monday	1
Tuesday	3
Wednesday	5.5
Thursday	8.5
Friday	6
Saturday	6
Sunday	7

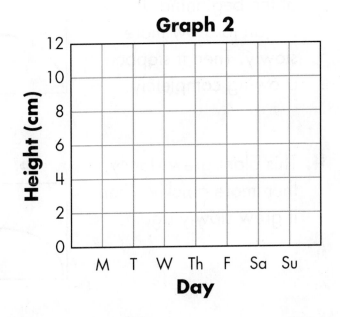

Graph 2

Choose the Graph

Choose the graph that matches the description.

1. This plant did not grow steadily.

Plant A

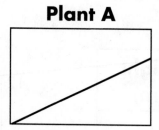

Plant B

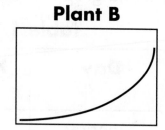

2. This plant grew more quickly at the beginning.

Plant A

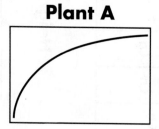

Plant B

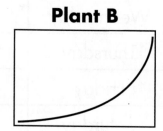

3. This plant grew quickly at the beginning. It began to grow more slowly. Then it stopped growing completely.

Plant A

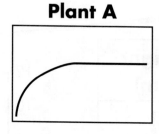

Plant B

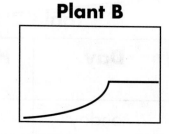

4. This plant grew slowly, then more quickly. Then it grew slowly again.

Plant A

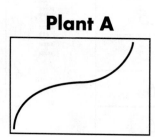

Plant B

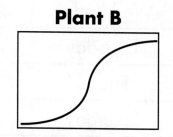